# DESIGN FOR DEMENTIA

*Margaret P. Calkins, M. Arch.*

# DESIGN FOR DEMENTIA
## Planning Environments for
## the Elderly and the Confused

**NHP** National Health Publishing
*A Division of Williams & Wilkins*

*Published by*
National Health Publishing
99 Painters Mill Road
Owings Mills, Maryland 21117
(301) 363-6400

*A division of Williams & Wilkins*

*Printed in the United States of America*
*Second Printing*

*Acquisitions Editor:* Sara Mansure Sides
*Developmental Editor:* Amy Kilgallon
*Production Coordinator:* Karen Babcock
*Design:* Sandy Renovetz
*Compositor:* National Health Publishing
*Printer:* Port City Press

ISBN: 0-932500-93-5
LC: 88-61561

# Dedication

---

"Don't try so hard to build a memory; just make each moment count."

> Mary Risse
> Mt. Carmel
> Health Care Center

This book is dedicated with respect and admiration to those who are concerned with making life the best it can be for the victims of Alzheimer's disease and related disorders.

# Contents

# Part II—Designing the Solution

# List of Figures

# *Foreword*

Alzheimer's disease has reached public consciousness in the past decade with amazing speed, considering that this disease, under this name or other names such as "senility," has been recognized for centuries. With such high awareness it is likely that any book offering some hope regarding efforts to better deal with this illness would be viewed as valuable. We are very fortunate that this first attempt to address questions regarding the design of environments for Alzheimer's victims is both professionally of high quality and, at the same time, highly usable by people who want to apply its scientifically-based insights. The perspective of this book is scrupulously honest from a scientific point of view. The pressure to find solutions to the problem of Alzheimer's disease could easily lead to unrealistic claims for any new approach. This book is careful to avoid such claims and to concentrate on the possibilities for incremental improvement that are inherent in the behavioral design approach.

The push to deal with Alzheimer's disease has tended to focus our attention on the biology of the illness and an eventual pharmacological treatment. Whether or not such an orientation is reasonable (and it may well be), such a focus has the great disadvantage of appearing to downgrade the potential of other approaches to the management of people with this illness. The author could be considered almost radical in suggesting that one of these nonbiological management techniques is worth serious attention. For most of this century, people have reacted to "senility" and its related conditions with nihilism and resignation. If we can demonstrate that, in fact, something can be done for the patient, we shall be partly on the way toward a more optimistic approach.

The big problem is in defining what can be done in concrete terms where we can specify what we wish to accomplish, how we shall recognize progress when we see it, and then, finally, what we need to apply as the agent of change. The author has rightly noted the need for a clear definition of a goal for a special unit of the type under discussion. The larger goal must then be elaborated by more specific objectives—objectives which are likely to be small. To a grieving or anxious family member, the goal for an afflicted parent may very understandably be originally seen as a cure, a reversal, or a return to the parent or spouse they used to know.

The administrator, the designer, and the treatment staff of the special unit are in an excellent position to educate the family member in the meaning of small increments of positive change. It is in such incremental terms that we have evidence that positive change can occur. For example, a person can become less anxious by coming to recognize where she is at a given moment. Another person can be taught by psychological conditioning methods to cease shouting. Yet another may experience an hour of watching interesting behavior by sensitive attention to where he sits, as contrasted with an hour of literal sensory deprivation consequent to having the choice only of sitting in his bedroom.

Each of these examples represents a gain because an increment of independence is attained, whether by having knowledge of one's environment, increasing one's social skill, or being able to learn by watching. None of these increments cure the illness. But can there be any argument that becoming more independent, or getting more stimulation, is preferable to dependence or stimulus poverty?

The design of the care environment is based exactly on this incremental philosophy. Ms. Calkins notes the "prosthetic" nature of environmental intervention, in contrast to the "therapeutic" ideal of acute medical care.

The excellent feature of environment as prosthesis is that the environment is always there. It can act as a prosthesis to enhance that increment of independence or stimulation.

Particularly laudable is the author's continued concern over the way the special care environment is used by those who populate it. She is acutely aware that administrators and treatment staff are a vital aspect of the environment, as much as is the physical design.

The approach taken in this book will be of inestimable value in orienting these users of the environment to the reasons for the way the unit is structured. We typically think of a brilliant design as capable of carrying its own message. To say that the physical care environment is there all the time is not meant to characterize that brilliant design as a treatment agent in its own right; the physical environment is not an "agent". It is there, but there to be used by those who know how to use it.

I have argued repeatedly that the later stages of a complete design process must include a phase of training users to get the most out of their environment. This book makes it clear, as separate physical elements are discussed in relation to their more abstract goals, just what the thinking is behind literally hundreds of informed design decisions. This book is extremely usable for in-service training purposes.

The fact is that user training cannot be called a "phase" of the design process; rather, it is a repetitive element that is necessary, not only because staff members forget, but because of staff turnover as well.

In combination with training to use what is already given in the structure of the care environment, an even more creative spark may be lit by the staff's knowledge that they can learn to apply the same design principles more actively on their own initiative. An environment of the type treated in this book is always a changing environment. If staff have the basic sensitization and a little know-how about behavioral design they can become active participants in the evolution of the care environment. It has been noted repeatedly that many direct care staff enjoy the role of decorator or arranger of new reinforcing properties of a treatment situation. With encouragement they will be alert to the need for changes in furnishings, decor, orientational devices, or physical features that convey information.

To conclude, although this book represents the state of knowledge in prosthetic design for the Alzheimer's patient, it is also extremely clear in its ability to teach the principles behind the design. Thus it ought to have as much use in treatment settings as in architects' or administrators' offices.

M. Powell Lawton, Ph.D.
Director of Research
Philadelphia Geriatric Center

# *Acknowledgments*

My thanks go to the people at all the facilities I have visited—the administrators, nurses, social workers and aides—for sharing their thoughts, plans, techniques, and dreams for creating sensitive and supportive environments for their residents with Alzheimer's disease and related disorders. To the staff and residents at Northview Home, Waukesha, Wisconsin, and Heather Hill, Chardon, Ohio, I am grateful for the continual support of, and enthusiasm for, my endeavors. I thank Laurie Hackett, Sherry Ahrentzen and Chari Weber for contributing their time, experience and wisdom. My deepest respect and gratitude to my parents, who have shared with me their humanistic and optimistic approach to life. And, finally, my utmost thanks and respect go to Jerry Weisman who has been a continual source of support and inspiration, and without whom this book would not have been possible.

# Introduction

The potential of the physical environment to play an active role in shaping and supporting human lives is a concept that has only recently begun to gain acceptance. Research on psychological and social environments has been accumulating and generating interest for centuries. But it is only within the past 20 years that systematic examination of the role of the physical environment in shaping lives has begun.

Much of the early work on the effects of environment was conducted by psychologists, social and behavioral scientists who "typically viewed the physical environment as the passive background of man's behavior rather than as a dynamic shaper of human events" (Holahan 1972, 115). The focus was on understanding this person–environment relationship from the psychological and behavioral point of view. Consequently, results were couched in terms of broad theoretical constructs on a macroenvironmental scale; typical studies explored the negative effects of crowding (Altman 1975; Esser 1979; Freedman 1975); and environmental press and its relation to competence (Lawton 1977b, 1981). These constructs are important and necessary for understanding the relationship of the physical environment to the people within it. They are used to formulate the basis of many research projects. However, the results of these studies are often not presented in ways that allow the *designer* to make practical use of the knowledge gained.

the results of these studies are often not presented in ways that allow the *designer* to make practical use of the knowledge gained.

More recent investigations have begun to direct attention towards increasing understanding of the microenvironment: lighting, acoustics, and room size, and scale. While work in this area is still sparse (Howell 1980; Hiatt 1985), efforts are being made to conduct the research so that the resulting hypotheses and information are useful to architects, interior designers, and others in the design fields who need this material to help them create "better" environments.

As awareness of the effects of the physical environment increases, attention is being focused on those populations which could benefit the most from this greater understanding. There is evidence suggesting that the low-competent are the group most sensitive to the physical environment (Lawton 1981; Nelson and Paluck 1980). Competence, as defined by Lawton (1977a, 8-9 ), refers to:

> the givens within the individual such as physical or mental health, intellectual capacity or ego strength...lowered competence may result from poor physical health, age-related sensory losses, mental health problems and so on....As individual competence decreases, the environment assumes increasing importance in determining well-being. One corollary of this hypothesis is that the low-competent are increasingly sensitive to noxious environments. The opposite, more positive corollary is that a small environmental improvement may produce a disproportionate amount of improvement in affect or behavior in the low-competent individual.

The normal aging process produces sensory losses, decreased muscle strength and reflex time, and diminished energy levels, all of which will compromise the ability of the elderly individual to cope with the environment. When these declines are coupled with the progressive cognitive losses associated with a dementing disorder like

Alzheimer's disease, the person is even less competent and able to cope. As Hall and Buckwalter (1987, 7) write, "logic suggest that persons with SDAT (senile dementia of the Alzheimer's type) need their environmental demands modified to compensate for their declining ability to adapt."

Alzheimer's disease and the related dementias (which will hereafter be referred to as ARD)—have received national attention recently. There is no cure or effective treatment at this point, but millions of dollars are being spent on efforts to develop effective medical treatment. Federal funding for research on dementia has risen from 3.8 million in 1976 to 50.8 million in 1985, and an estimated 12.8 billion was spent on care of the affected population. Until such time as a cure is found and is readily available to everyone, concentrated efforts must be made to improve the quality of life for those who are afflicted with these devastating diseases.

Unfortunately, this effort is not now being made. Hiatt (1985, 2), in an excellent paper, reports the following:

> Recently, I had the opportunity to review over a dozen programs identified by the sponsors and one or more outsiders as innovative. I was surprised to find that 1) few were based upon a clear understanding of the dynamics of Alzheimer's, information on learning or attention span or even literature reporting what has (or has not) worked; 2) few involved some overall plan or concept; 3) many included a pastiche of activities focused on fact drills (reality orientation), though this represents a simplistic notion of memory (Zepelin, et al., 1981).

This description of current management techniques suggests that there has been little realization of the potential use of the physical environment as a therapeutic tool, even in settings where, as Lawton suggests, such use is most likely to be beneficial.

Why is it so important to look at the physical environment as a therapeutic tool? There are those who say that good staff can overcome a bad environment. There are others who express the belief that Alzheimer's and similarly afflicted patients are "too far gone" to even be aware of their environment. There is, however, evidence indicating that special attention to the physical and social environments of the cognitively impaired older person can maintain and/or increase their functional capacity, self-respect, and dignity (Lawton 1981; Nelson and Paluck 1980). The following statements support that conclusion.

> A growing body of literature indicates that architectural and physical design features of sheltered care facilities can affect the behavior and functioning of elderly people (Bednar 1977; Koncelik 1976; Lawton 1977). . . . Carp (1976, 1977) had noted...that positive physical qualities of the housing environment can influence an elderly person's activity level, social contacts, well-being and general life style (Moos and Lemke 1980, 571).

> The results. . . point to the value of having nursing home staff and consultants approach a facility's environment as though the environment itself represented an important treatment intervention. The findings indicate that specific environmental factors have as much influence on residents' integration as does their level of physical and psychosocial functioning (Kruzich 1984, 14).

There is also evidence (Moos and Igra 1980) suggesting that architectural and policy features are more important than building or facility type in determining the social environment.

While there is research to support the theory that the physical environment does have an impact on behavior, little has been done to examine the effect of particular elements of the environment. What work has been done in this area has focused on the cognitively intact elderly, who are more capable of coping with problems in the environment. For the purposes of this book, therefore, it was necessary to extrapolate and synthesize from literature on the diseases themselves and their typical behavioral manifestations information on the effects—both positive and negative—of the physical environment. It became clear that many of the behavioral criteria and design responses cited in those studies are applicable to the cognitively intact elderly, and to a wide range of environmental types, from traditional integrated nursing homes to special care units, assisted living arrangements, and the home environment.

# About This Book

Since many long-term care facilities have made the decision to segregate cognitively impaired patients from more intact residents (see Chapter 2 for more on this topic), the decision was made to focus in this volume primarily on special care units for the cognitively impaired. Some of the design suggestions are based on particular types of units or floor plans (i.e., a corridor with rooms along both sides as opposed to an open plan with rooms around a central space). An attempt was made to provide a variety of responses or design criteria, since every institution has its own building constraints within which to work. Recognition of and response to other constraints, such as costs and budgetary concerns, nursing/staff ratios, staffing patterns, and administrative policies was also made.

Many of the design criteria are applicable to other settings and groups. For example, all elderly experience changes in sensory perception, increasing their sensitivity to glare. Therefore non-reflective surfaces should be used in all environments where the older person is likely to be. Any design response which is equally applicable to all elderly has been so designated with an [E]. In addition, the [H] symbol is used to highlight issues which are important for the cognitively impaired person still living at home. For example, an extra power switch or timer on the stove can prevent a disaster.

This book is divided into two sections. Part I begins with a description of Alzheimer's disease and the related dementias (ARD's) and the implications for environment–behavior relationships. Chapter 2 discusses the importance of having a well-developed, well-understood organizational philosophy when setting up a special care unit for an ARD population. The chapter stresses the importance of a holistic approach that combines environmental considerations with special programs and activities. Chapter 3 examines five areas of person–environment interaction which are particularly relevant to persons with ARD. Chapter 4 outlines strategies for environmental intervention, ranging from the importance of a residential character to the use of prosthetic supports.

Part II is a design guide. Chapter 5 examines issues and design responses which are not particular to a single area or room, but relate to the design of special care units as a whole. Chapters 6 through 13 discuss each area of a special care unit in terms of the person–environment interactions, presenting design responses and suggesting solutions to problems. Each subsection of each chapter in the design guide (e.g., way-finding for bedrooms) contains a variety of illustrative examples. These examples were selected to expose the reader to a range of possible design responses. Some are unique or especially creative, and cannot easily be integrated with or adapted to existing buildings. Nevertheless, they might stimulate new ideas when working within the parameters of specific facilities. Most of the sample designs however, were selected because of their adaptability to a variety of building types and plan configurations. The final chapter is a design review checklist. It is intended to be used as a rating scale to evaluate the environmental characteristics of existing or proposed units.

*Design for Dementia* is not a cookbook; one cannot just put the various ingredients or environmental characteristics together and come up with the "right" answer or "best" design for a special care unit. The book is a survey of the important issues which need to be taken into account when designing an environment for a cognitively impaired population, and a source of suggestions for resolving those issues.

It is intended and hoped that this book will be used by a variety of groups. It will provide designers—both architects and interior designers—information about the special needs of the ARD population. In addition to providing a basic understanding of the diseases courses and ramifications, which is absolutely crucial to sensitive, supportive design, *Design for Dementia* presents results of recent research on the influence of specific environmental elements on the lives of persons with ARD.

This book is also intended to be used by administrators and staff of care facilities, to help increase awareness of how the physical environment can be seen and used as a therapeutic tool to support the programs and activities for residents.

Finally, anyone caring for a person with ARD at home should be able to use this book to understand what environmental modifications may be appropriate and needed in the home. The final chapter can also act as a guide to help families evaluate, and eventually select, a good long term care facility when the time comes.

Optimally, this book will serve as a tool to enhance communication between all parties involved in creating a special unit for the cognitively impaired. Again, the solutions presented here are not meant to be "right," or to be the only approaches to design and care problems. Every facility planning a special care unit has its own staffing patterns, population, program, budget, and, often, existing building. It must be recognized and remembered that design does not occur in a void. It must be interwoven with these and other factors. The information presented here should suggest starting points. It is up to each facility's staff and designers to find the right solutions for their particular situation.

# *About the Author*

---

Margaret P. Calkins is a Design Specialist with Heather Hill, Inc., a nursing home and rehabilitation hospital in Chardon, Ohio and a Design Consultant affiliated with Health Consultants International.

Ms. Calkins graduated from Kenyon College with a B.A. degree in psychology and received her Masters of Architecture from the University of Wisconsin at Milwaukee. Ms. Calkins was awarded the American Institute of Architects/American Hospital Association Graduate Fellowship in Health Facilities Design Research. She also received a first place award in the Association of Collegiate Schools of Architecture, West Central Regional Student Research Competition. She is currently a member of the Gerontological Society of America and the Environmental Design Research Association.

*Part I*

---

# Understanding
# the Problem

# Chapter 1

# Characteristics of Dementia

## Introduction

The design of sensitive, therapeutically supportive physical environments for the cognitively impaired elderly requires an understanding of the basic needs of this special population. While it is beyond the scope of this book to provide in-depth insight into the changes produced by ARD, a brief description of the disease and its effects is in order. There are many more behavioral consequences of the disease within the afflicted population than are described in this chapter. Those chosen for discussion are the most important to the design of the physical environment.

## Epidemiology and Symptoms

It has been said that Alzheimer's disease is the most prevalent and the most devastating illness of the aged. It must be made clear, however, that this statement actually refers to Alzheimer's disease *and related disorders* (ARDs) which are grouped under the heading of dementia. In the United States, dementing illness ranks as the fourth leading cause of death among all individuals over 65 years of age, following heart disease, cancer, and stroke. From 1.5–3 million Americans suffer from some form of dementia.

3

Dementia is not a disease. It is a description of a group of symptoms, primarily including gradual but progressive loss of intellectual function and memory, confusion, personality change, impaired judgment and reasoning capabilities, and depression. Alzheimer's disease is only one type of dementia, but it is the most prevalent, constituting almost 50% of all dementia cases. Other common causes of dementia include multiple strokes, heart attacks, thyroid problems, and nutritional deficiencies (Mace and Rabins 1981; Atlanta ADRDA 1985).

The ARDs are complex and affect people in different ways. While each disease has its own etiology, many of the behavioral characteristics are similar and, for the purposes of this book, the differences among the dementing illnesses are not as important as their similarities. A good general description was provided by the U.S. Department of Health and Human Services (1984, 3).

> At first, the individual with Alzheimer's disease experiences only minor and almost imperceptible symptoms that are often attributed to emotional upsets or other physical illnesses. Gradually, however, the person becomes more forgetful— particularly about recent events—and this may be reported by anxious relatives. The person may neglect to turn off the stove, may misplace things, may recheck to see if a task was done, may take longer to complete a chore that was previously routine, or may repeat already answered questions. As the disease progresses, memory loss and changes in personality, mood and behavior including confusion, irritability, restlessness, and agitation are likely to appear. Judgement, concentration, orientation, writing, reading, speech, motor behavior and naming of objects may also be affected.

## Implications for Facility Planners

A facility providing quality care for ARD residents, must offer appropriate care strategies for residents throughout the progressive, degenerative course of dementing disease. Cohen, Kennedy, and Eisdorfer (1984) have developed a model using six psychosocial phases to help planners conceptualize the process of change in the person with ARD. The six stages are:

1) Prediagnosis: Recognition and concern. Cognitive problems are subtle, but eventually progress from simple error to the point where they interfere with daily life.

2) Reaction to diagnosis: Denial. Patients and families often deny the existence of the disease, which interferes with the early implementation of any therapeutic plans.

3) Following the diagnosis: Anger, guilt and sadness. The disease is incorporated into the daily life of the person with ARD and his or her family. It is important to stress the patient's existing abilities, not those that have been lost.

4) Coping. Patterns for coping with diminishing capabilities are established.

5) Maturation. The person is unable to function independently, and is often placed in an institution.

6) Separation from self. At this point, the individual's cognitive abilities have deteriorated to such a degree that no meaningful interaction with other people or the environment is possible.

While ARDs are highly individualistic, with patients exhibiting different functional deficits at various stages of the disease, there are some common behavioral patterns. A brief review of the particular characteristics of dementia which are most affected by the environment will help administrators, staff, families, and designers have a greater understanding of how physical surroundings can affect patients, and indicate ways in which the environment can be used as a therapeutic tool.

*Memory*

The essence of dementia is deterioration of intellect and mental capabilities. There is a difference between "memory loss" and simple "forgetfulness." Memory loss, as found in demented persons, means that lost thoughts cannot be retrieved; in forgetfulness, which happens to everyone, a lost idea is eventually recovered. In dementia, memory loss is progressive and eventually has a profound effect on daily life.

There is some indication (Nebes et al. 1984) that semantic memory (a basically context-free thesaurus of knowledge) is less affected by dementing disease than is episodic memory (the mental record of events in a person's life), especially in the earlier stages of the illness. Furthermore, memories of distant events are retained longer than those of more recent occurrences, adding to the person's overall feeling of confusion. Residents of special care units will not be able to rely on memory for help in their environmental interactions; hence, the environment must be readily understandable by someone who is unfamiliar with it. For example, easy-to-read clocks and large wall calendars can help orient someone who has trouble tracking the passage of time. Because changes are especially difficult for the cognitively impaired person to understand and cope with, an environment that is familiar (i.e., related to previously experienced environments) will be easier for the resident to understand because it is more likely to be linked with remaining memories.

*Orientation*

Wandering is a common phenomenon among people with dementia. It might reflect anxiety, boredom, restlessness, or simply a need for exercise. In addition, wandering can be caused by an inability to orient oneself within a space. A person who wants to go to his or her room but cannot find it might walk into every room in the area before recognizing the one that is "home." An environment that is designed to provide cues and information about specific room locations and functions will help residents make their way through a unit unassisted. Special attention also needs to be given to keeping residents out of potentially dangerous areas. Staff members who perceive an environment as unsafe are more likely to actively restrict residents with either medication or physical restraints.

*Complex Tasks*

People with dementia become progressively less capable of completing complex tasks (like balancing a checkbook), a problem related to memory loss. As the disease progresses, more and more tasks become too complex, until the act of dressing or zipping up a zipper might be beyond the person's capacity. Even fairly late-stage ARD victims might still be able to complete complex tasks when those tasks are broken down into a series of simpler activities, but they might need assistance in remembering the proper task order. The environment can help by providing cues to or information about appropriate steps or tasks, or by making resident–environment interactions easy to understand and manipulate.

*Activity Levels*

The onset of dementia is often accompanied by an apparent increased activity level. There is some indication that ARD persons who were active before becoming ill will continue to be highly active throughout the disease (Robb and Monsour 1980). High activity levels might also be more noticeable in dementing diseases because the person is not engaged in useful, satisfying tasks.

The ARD person's environment needs to accommodate this increased activity level. A safe "wandering path" with interesting views, "tasks" to do along the way, and access to frequently populated areas will allow residents to burn off some of their excess energy in a nondestructive way. Access to objects like books or a basket of laundry to fold provides other outlets for energy.

*Agitation*

Either frustration at the inability to do tasks that were once simple or confusion about the environment, can cause the person with dementia to become agitated. Some people are in an almost constant state of agitation. In addition, people with cognitive impairments often overreact to seemingly minor problems. This is called catastrophic reaction, and can happen at any time. It is helpful for care personnel to be aware of the causes of a catastrophic reaction: feelings of being overwhelmed by an environment or experience, of being lost or abandoned, or of being frightened by strange people. Overstimulation, from noise or activities, can also cause this behavior.

One environmental way to cope with catastrophic reactions is to remove the person to a smaller, more manageable environment. A "quiet room" away from the activity on the unit is often a good solution. It must be remembered that placing a resident in a quiet room is not punishment, but rather is a chance to help the person regain control and to provide some privacy. It also might be possible to avoid catastrophic reactions altogether by creating an environment which does not provide undue visual or acoustic stimulation. For instance, smaller spaces are usually easier for the person with dementia to understand and cope with than are larger areas. In addition, generous use of sound-absorbing materials is essential.

## Other Design Considerations

While the primary concern in the design of an ARD care environment should be the special needs of the residential population, the needs of the other users must also be considered. Unit staff and families of residents are also affected by the physical and social environment of the special care unit. Their needs differ from the residents, and must also be taken into account. An environment which supports residents' needs *and* staff functions can increase job satisfaction, reduce turnover caused by burn-out, improve morale, and more. While there has been no published research on staff attitudes about special care units for people with dementia, there have been studies on facilities for mentally retarded adults (Tjosvold and Tjosvold 1983; Holland et al. 1981). Kruzich (1986, 16) has pointed out the relationship between resident progress and staff performance: "Numerous studies in residential care facilities for the mentally retarded indicate that staff members are more likely to feel satisfied and committed to the facility when residents are learning and increasing their skills."

In looking at staff needs, the nurse's station and its location emerge as primary design concerns. There is no "right way" to design a nurse's station. Facility administrators and staff might decide that, in order to create a homelike environment, the nurse's station should be simply a conveniently located desk; or they might decide that a large, "landmark" nurse's station is appropriate. Either arrangement can work well if used to its best advantage. But any nursing station that separates the staff from the resident population will be counter productive, hindering the staff–resident interaction which is so important in an ARD care setting.

Another consideration is staff respite. There needs to be a staff lounge and bathroom area away from the unit. The stress of providing care for a cognitively impaired population is high, and breaks are essential to help staff members maintain the efficiency, patience, and perspective they need to do their jobs effectively.

Families and visitors must also be considered when designing a special care environment. It has been said that Alzheimer's takes its largest toll on family members, by forcing them to watch a loved one die twice: first in mind and then in body. The emotional strain is tremendous, and should be recognized by professional caregivers. There should be a room available where families can be alone to come to terms with their own feelings, or to have small group discussions with the staff. Many facilities have found that catering to the needs of the family is at least as important as supporting the needs of the residents. The unit environment should be one that families find comfortable and that allows both private time with the ill relative(s) and the opportunity to participate in public, group activities. There is, in addition, some indication that families visit more frequently when they are comfortable with the physical environment.

*Chapter 2*

# Organizational

# Philosophy

## Introduction

The successful development and creation of a special care unit for cognitively impaired older persons requires coordination of all elements of the total institutional environment. A physical environment that is supportive and provides opportunities for more enriching resident interaction, but is combined with staff members who do not know how to take advantage of environmental tools, or with an organizational policy that counteracts the positive effects of a therapeutic environment will not result in a unit which caters to and supports the special needs of the ARD population.

## The Caregiving Facility as a Total Environment

It is imperative that a caregiving institution set out its goals clearly, and then work in all areas to achieve them. To succeed, it is necessary to first understand the nursing facility as a total environment. One of the most commonly used models is based on a tripartite system (Marsh 1981; Weisman 1981b) that revolves around (1) the people within the setting, (2) the physical environment, and (3) the managing organization and its goals and policies. Weisman (1981b, 34) argues that each of these three subsets of the

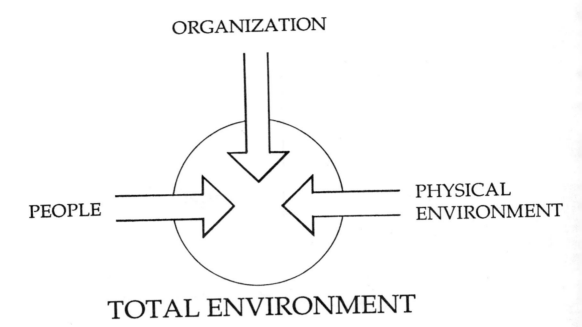

ORGANIZATION

PEOPLE

PHYSICAL
ENVIRONMENT

TOTAL ENVIRONMENT

*Figure 2-1 Model of
the Total Environment.*

total environment can be defined on two levels:

1) People have long range goals which serve to shape their everyday patterns of behavior.

2) The organization has long range goals or objectives which affect day-to-day policies and their implementation.

3) The physical setting has the actual components or elements (e.g., furniture and walls) and sensory and spatial properties (lighting, sounds, temperature).

It is the combination of these three subsystems which, in effect, creates the environment as experienced (see Figure 2-1).

*Institutionality*

To fully appreciate the holistic approach of Weisman's model, it is helpful to explore the concept of "institutionality." Traditionally, the dichotomy of "institutional" versus "residential" has been used to describe not only the physical environment (sterile vs. homey or rich), but also the balance of control. In an "institutional" setting, the administration and staff have control and set schedules and activities to meet their own needs. Conversely, in a "residential" setting, there is more of a balance of control among staff, administration, and residents. The King and Raynes Patient Management Scale was developed in 1968 to measure the "institutional" characteristics of an environment. It conceptualizes four dimensions of residential control: (1) rigid daily routines; (2) social distance between staff and residents; (3) depersonalizing care practices, including lack of privacy; and (4) blocking (e.g., the extent to which all residents must perform activities at the same time). (Kruzich and Berg 1985). Use of this tool can help a facility measure the extent to which its policies are "institutional." Moos and Igra's (1980) study on the determinants of the social environment also supports this holistic model. Their results indicate that policy and architectural features are stronger determinants of the social environment than is the facility type (skilled nursing, residential care, apartments).

In an ideal world, with unlimited resources, a facility would be able to completely meet each resident's individual needs and goals. Unfortunately, reality paints a different picture. The residents might prefer family style meals with some people eating at 5:00 P.M. and some at 7:00 P.M. The facility, in an effort to make sure that all residents eat complete and balanced meals, dictates meal times and serves food on trays. Some residents prefer eating alone, but the dining room seats 50 or more. Some residents prefer single rooms, but the facility only has double occupancy rooms, and residents are placed in any available bed, not necessarily with a roommate they would choose.

The resolution of these and other conflicts is not easy. At best, there will be compromises made by all three sub-groups. However, the situation is frequently perceived—on all sides—in terms of conflict, the needs and desires of the residents "against" the dictates of the organization. The potential role of the physical environment is often not realized. Yet, that environment can often provide the solutions to these apparent conflicts of interest.

*Setting Goals for the Special Care Unit*

Before the role of the physical environment is explored, it is helpful—in fact critical—to set forth goals for the ARD unit. What are, or should be, the goals of a special care unit? They will differ somewhat for every facility, but a review of the literature on this topic reveals several key objectives. One central theme runs through many of the articles: maximizing the functional independence of the residents. To quote Cohen, Kennedy, and Eisdorfer (1984):

> The treatment objectives for the care of older persons afflicted with Alzheimer's disease or a related disorder are to maximize their functional effectiveness, freedom, and human dignity. . . . Although the individual gradually becomes less competent, the challenge. . . . is to recognize residual strengths in the patient.(11).

> Maintaining physical health and mobility are primary objectives. . . . Other primary needs of the patient are to maintain his or her dignity, avoid dependency, be accepted by others, maintain interpersonal relationships and *establish a sense of self-control as well as control over the immediate environment* (14). (Italics added.)

*Helping Residents Feel "in Control"*

The loss of functional independence or control over one's life has serious negative repercussions; indeed, control or perceived control is a central component of self-respect and dignity (Glass and Singer 1971, 1972; Geer and Maisel 1972; Seligman 1975; Schulz 1976). In 1984, Eisdorfer (p. 39) wrote:

> One of the absolutely traumatic and debilitating processes in the human existence is the loss of mastery over your own life. . . . The data are unequivocal that loss of mastery leads to increased dependency and dementia. You take away the decision making capacity and people lose the capacity to make decisions.

While the loss of some functional independence during the first five stages of a dementing disease (see Cohen et al. 1984) and most (if not all) functional independence in the sixth stage is inevitable, it is necessary to ensure that the individual suffers only those losses caused by the disease. Schulz (1976) has shown that some characteristics commonly seen in the aged, including depression, helplessness, and rapid physical decline, can, at least in part, be due to a loss of control over one's life or surroundings. Lack of control also has significant impact on cognitive, emotional, and motivational responses. (For more information, see Averill 1973; Baum and Singer 1980; Lazarus 1966; Schulz 1976; Kahana 1975).

E

Schultz (1976) demonstrated that, even in the absence of real control, the illusion of control can have positive consequences. Other studies have linked control with predictability. There is evidence to suggest that the ability to reliably predict when, where, and for how long positive or negative events are likely to happen is almost as beneficial as actual control over these occurrences (Geer and Maisel 1972; Langer and Rodin 1976; Seligman 1975; White 1959; all cited in Pinet 1985). These studies indicate that the effects of control and predictability are as positive for the institutionalized elderly as they are for the population at large. Indeed, the control older people exert over their environment can bear a critical relationship to their well-being in other areas. It can enhance one's self-perception and sense of self-worth (White 1959, Pinet 1985). One Canadian study found that environmental factors accounted for 57% of the variation in self-esteem in deinstitutionalized developmentally disabled persons (Hull and Thompson 1981). The most important environmental factors cited in that study were opportunities for freedom and initiative and lack of unnecessary rules—i.e., control over events in one's own life (Hull and Thompson 1981; Kruzich and Berg 1985).

Control and predictability are important issues for everyone—young or old, healthy or ill/impaired. Some people are better able to cope with lack of control and predictability; they have the ability to make the changes necessary to increase control/predictability, or to leave the undesirable environment. The institutionalized and frail, however, often lack these capabilities. It is necessary, therefore, to find other ways of providing or allowing residents to exert control.

*Reconciling Resident-Oriented and Institution-Oriented Goals*

Residents' needs are not the only concern on special care units, or indeed on any nursing home unit. The needs, goals, and policies of the caregiving institution are also important, but, as indicated previously, do not always match the perceived or actual needs of the residents. The problem, then, becomes one of either creating ways to merge the goals of the two groups, or finding ways to provide for the needs of the residents without obstructing goals set for the facility itself. Perceived control and predictability can provide this fusion (Kruzich and Berg 1985; Holland et al. 1981; Kruzich and Berg (205) observe that:

> Those facilities with rigid and highly routinized schedules will, all other things being equal, have

lower levels of self-sufficiency among the residents.
. . . Facilities in which the activities are governed
with some degree of discretion and flexibility will,
all other things being equal, have higher levels of
self-sufficiency.

For example, allowing residents to decide on the type
of music played on the unit gives them a form of control
without interfering with institutional goals. Also, flexibility
on the part of the staff and support personnel can be used
to fulfill residents' needs. If the kitchen staff is flexible and
willing to serve at least some meals family style, and if staff
are trained and willing to take the extra time necessary to
ensure that the residents are getting enough food, it is
possible to make the dining experience more familiar and
pleasant for the residents.

Having established that the facility's primary goal
should be to maximize the functional independence of the
resident, the administration must decide how, and to what
extent, to mesh this with its own internal goals. To do this,
it is necessary to explore the particular ways in which the
resident-oriented goals can be accomplished. Hiatt (1985),
in an excellent article, lists 20 goals for a special care unit.
The list is comprehensive, and combines the three
subcategories in the model described earlier (see Figure 2-
1). The 20 goals are listed in Table 2-1 and divided into three
groups: (1) those providing general goals to work toward,
(2) those involving strategies for staff intervention, and (3)
specific environmental characteristics of an effective special
care unit.

Hiatt's goals demonstrate the necessity of a holistic
approach to the creation of special care units for cognitively
impaired older persons. The social, emotional, and physical
environments are all important and must be considered
carefully in order to maximize functional independence.
Another factor which needs to be considered carefully is
the segregation or integration of the ARD population with
the facility's healthier, cognitively intact residents. Many
people feel that the negative aspects of such integration

H

**Table 2-1** Programmatic and Environmental Goals for Special Care Units

**Resident Centered Goals**

1) Maximize attention span or moments of alertness.

2) Increase feelings of security, comfort, and emotional well-being.

3) Allow release of anxiety, frustration, and agitation.

4) Deal creatively with paradoxes: the need for stimulation versus the problem of overstimulation; the need for predictability versus the value of prompting curious inquiry through change; the need for social interaction versus the importance of "time out" or "one-li-ness."

5) Maintain maximum levels of self-care and dignity in toileting, grooming, dressing, and interpersonal behavior.

6) Allow individuals to function at an appropriate pace and time schedule.

7) Prevent unnecessary deterioration, suffering, or worry about memory loss through programming and services.

8) Provide residents access to organized worship and/or personally meaningful religious expression.

**Staff Centered Goals**

E

9) Recognize and respond to residents' inability to distinguish between fact, action and emotion.

10) Attempt to elicit speech or nonverbal communication, normal interactions, and individually appropriate behavior.

11) Interact directly with individual residents rather than speaking around, behind, or over them, even if their own communication is nonverbal.

12) Minimize the use of physical and/or pharmacologic restraints and controlling devices in cooperation with families.

13) Evaluate and reevaluate the program and facilities continuously; do not expect to find one caregiving approach that is suitable for all residents. . . or at all times

**Table 2-1,** continued.

### Environment Centered Goals

14) Maximize independence in activities of daily living (ADLs): self-feeding (even if it means more meals or preparation of "finger," rather then pureed, foods), dignified and enjoyable bathing, gracious grooming, personalized dressing, etc.

15) Offer natural outlets for the need to exercise, for fresh air and motion.

16) Use environmental design, cues, and props, in addition to programs and social experiences, to connect residents with their pasts: with memories, familiar experiences, and emotions.

17) Draw upon visual, audio, tactile, olfactory, and kinesthetic resources to help residents compensate for sensory losses and utilize remaining abilities.

18) Design spaces to encourage formation of manageable-sized groups (2–3, 5–6 people) for social and program purposes rather than providing large areas drawing 20 or more people.

19) Control noxious stimuli (glare, noise) and social irritants (crowding, isolation, lack of tactile stimulation, excessive stimulation).

20) Provide comfortable areas for cognitively impaired residents to interact with families and friends in a manner which is as satisfying as possible for all that are involved.

outweigh the positive ones. "Healthy" residents don't always like to be with people who act inappropriately, who disrupt the daily routine, invade privacy, and go through others' personal belongings. Cognitively intact elderly persons are not always interested in helping impaired residents, and don't like to be reminded that such deterioration might be in their own futures.

It is, in part, because of the kinds or concerns just mentioned that people with dementia and/or behavior problems have traditionally been segregated. The general trend now remains in favor of segregation because of the special needs of the ARD population. Staff on Alzheimer's units are often given special training; programs and activities are geared specifically to the cognitively impaired; and the unit environment might be treated or organized differently from the rest of the facility to help compensate for the known deficits of this population. This is not to say that segregation is necessarily right for every facility. Some places find that integration works well, that staff are able to supervise and provide all the necessary components of quality care, and that cognitively intact residents do not mind and are in fact supportive of the more impaired population. In either case, any facility's physical environment can be modified to support residents' remaining capabilities and compensate for lost ones.

*Chapter 3*

# Environment and Behavior Issues

---

## Introduction

Two aspects of Weisman's model (see Chapter 2) have now been explored: resident/staff behaviors, characteristics, and needs and organizational philosophies and policies. But it is also important to understand how a facility's physical environment can be used effectively to achieve it's resident-oriented goals—to help residents have and maintain control and functional independence without giving up the administrative control it needs to run the unit safely and efficiently. To understand how to manipulate the environment to achieve operational goals, it is necessary first to understand how cognitively impaired residents interact with their physical surroundings.

Persons with dementia will experience profound changes—especially decreases—in their ability to understand and control interactions with the physical environment. No amount of physical or social environmental intervention can change that fact. However, while it is not possible to stop the progression of a dementing disease, it may be possible to effectively slow down the rate of deterioration. In one of the most comprehensive studies done in this area, Lawton (1981, 240), through the creation of a supportive physical environment, was able to show a lack of decline in basic indicators of competence over time in individuals with ARD. He suggested that this finding constitutes "indirect evidence of a prosthetic effect, and in some instances, a possible positive effect".

The deliberately simplistic model of environment–behavior interactions suggested in this book covers just five factors that are particularly important for the ARD population: way-finding/orientation, personalization, privacy and socialization, safety and security, and activities of daily living (ADLs). These interactions are examined from the environmental point of view; that is, it shows how to use the environment to affect the relationship, not just change the behavior of the individual.

Specific strategies for dealing with these issues are presented in the design guide (Part II).

## E

## Way-finding/Orientation

*Definition:*

The process by which the environment helps a person derive cues and information to aid in navigation from a point through space to a desired location.

The ability to navigate through the environment—to know where one is in relation to where one wants to be, and how to get from one point to another—is an important determinant of a person's feelings of autonomy, independence, and self-sufficiency. The environment can provide a variety of cues and means to help in this way-finding process. This information can range from actual sight of the desired goal and the path to it to landmarks (furniture, color, plants, rugs, almost anything) indicating present location, and/or directional signs (or lines on the floor) indicating the desired path, to people who act as guides.

In addition to environmental cues and information, memory and the ability to create cognitive maps also play vital roles in way-finding. The ability to form a mental map or plan of the building/space in which one is negotiating a path significantly increases the ability to successfully travel from the present location to a desired one. Also, a person who has "learned the way" doesn't have to attend to all of the cues on every trip through the area.

The ability of the cognitively impaired person to make mental maps of a building or space is severely limited, as is the ability to remember pathways on the basis of past experience, especially recent experience (Weber et al. 1978). Therefore, special attention must be paid to providing orientation cues/information within the special care environment. People with dementia are cognizant of and attuned to different elements and characteristics of the environment at different stages of their disease. Some are able to read and understand signs, while others have lost that ability. Therefore, multiple cuing, or providing the same information in several different ways, directed to several different senses, will provide pertinent information to a greater number of residents than would a single orientation cue. For example, some residents will be able to follow a sign indicating the direction to the toilets; others will recognize the brightly colored canopy over the door; some will need a line on the floor or wall from the dining room to the toilet rooms; and still others will need to be led by someone. The provision of this variety of cues will increase the potential for residents to find their own way.

E

## Privacy and Socialization

*Definition:*    The degree to which the environment inhibits or facilitates opportunities for a person to control amounts of privacy and social contact between people.

The option or opportunity to make decisions about privacy and social contact is important in every person's life. It can be especially important for institutionalized persons who have lost control of so may other aspects of their lives. The amount of control different institutions allow residents varies with a number of factors, including unit size, staffing ratios and patterns, organizational philosophy, and programming. In every setting, however, the opportunity for residents to have some control or perceived control over social interaction is important.

The frequent occurrence of null behavior (lack of any observable behavior or activity) in many nursing homes is well documented. The prevention of null behavior should be considered a high priority in any facility which aims to provide quality care (McClannaham 1973). Research indicates that null behavior is most likely to occur when residents do not have the opportunity to decide between privacy and socializing (Sommer 1969; Sommer and Dewar 1963; Sommer and Kroll 1979; Lawton, Leibowitz & Charon 1970).

Preventing null behavior is a complex matter which requires attention to both the physical and the social environments. The physical environment must provide opportunities for social contact, both casual and structured. On the social environmental side, staff often need to be trained to encourage resident interaction. There are also a variety of environmental supports which can enhance opportunities for social contact. Some are as simple as arranging chairs in small groups or around tables instead of having them lined up around the perimeter of a room. This makes communication between residents easier. Nooks along hallways allow residents to socialize casually in passing without interfering with traffic patterns (Lawton and Simon 1968). Doorways, recessed and grouped together, provide the same opportunity for contact with neighbors without being in the way.

As important as increased opportunities for social contact are, it is also necessary to allow residents the opportunity to choose when they want privacy. Pastalan's (1974), Sommer's (1969), and Lawton and Badar's (1970) research clearly indicates one positive effect of opportunities for privacy: increased social interaction.

Privacy requires visual and/or acoustic separation although no research has been conducted to determine which is more important for this population. In an institutional setting, small nooks in public areas allow residents to watch ongoing activities without necessarily participating. The opportunities for going to one's room, or to a special "quiet room," for some measure of privacy are other possibilities. The staff needs to be alert to residents' need for privacy, and trained to help satisfy it.

It can be concluded from existing research that an environment which provides opportunities for privacy and social interaction will decrease the incidence of null behavior. It will also allow residents one more measure of control over their lives and surroundings.

# E

## Personalization

*Definition:*

The degree to which the environment encourages or discourages residents' control over the placement and arrangement of personal effects.

The importance of the ability to personalize one's immediate surroundings cannot be overemphasized. It does more than make a place "look nice." It is a visible manifestation of a person's self-image. Throughout life, every person displays personal items, decorates walls, and arranges furniture to suit individual tastes. A personalized environment not only says who a person is, it clearly stakes out a territory—a place that is the individual's own. Territoriality is "the staking out of specific individual areas in space common to a group and is regarded as having an instinctual base" (Paluck and Esser 1971, 24). It allows a person to lay claim to an area and *have control over it.*

The move to an institution, and its accompanying loss of control, is traumatic for anyone, but can be especially difficult for the confused, cognitively impaired person. The transition from familiar to unfamiliar surroundings and routines can intensify confusional states and cause disruptive behaviors. Therefore, "some view territoriality as emerging and manifesting itself more intensely in regressed institutionalized populations" (Nelson and Paluck 1980, 29).

The ability to personalize one's environment has many advantages. It can add familiarity to the world, counteracting disruptive influences of unfamiliar surroundings. Display of personal items can also help persons maintain their "personal identities" longer; this can be crucial, especially in ARD victims whose illness is slowly robbing them of their identities. Personalization also gives special care residents another element of real or perceived control. And personalizing an environment requires no active manipulation or decision-making, once the living area is set up.

Altman (1975) describes two types of territoriality; primary and secondary. Personalization of the bedroom is a way to claim primary territory. Secondary territories might include, for instance, a specific place at the dinner table. The latter could be delineated with special chairs or decorations. Or residents could be encouraged to bring a favorite armchair with them to the facility. Such an item can be put into the living room, thus serving the dual purpose of providing secondary territorialities and increasing the familiarity of the environment. Personal items can also serve as landmarks and provide something for residents to talk about.

# H

## Safety and Security

*Definition:*

The degree to which the environment is designed to avoid the occurrence of accidents while not inhibiting ease of locomotion through, and use of, the area.

Because of the special problems of the ARD population, two types of safety/security issues must be considered: precautions necessitated by residents' physical impairments, and those made necessary by the cognitive impairments of the ARD population.

Most people with dementia are elderly. Even those who are younger often develop kinesthetic (balance) problems. A shuffling gait and propensity to falling are also common. Therefore, the environment must include the standard safety precautions that are taken for an older population (i.e., nonskid floors, clearly marked changes in level, sturdy hand rails).

Beyond these standard supports, the environment must be safe for cognitively impaired persons who might not follow typical behavior patterns. There are, basically, three levels of precautions, each allowing the ARD victim a different degree of control over the environment. All may be necessary in different parts of the same unit. These three levels are described in the following sections.

*No Access*

When areas of the environment or pieces of equipment are especially hazardous to impaired residents, access should be denied. This might be accomplished through locking doors to the outside, installing handles which residents cannot manipulate on the doors of closets containing hazardous materials, or locking off entire areas, such as the kitchen, except for scheduled therapeutic activities.

*Limited Access with Staff Supervision*

When access to areas or equipment is potentially hazardous to residents, but can be made safe with adequate supervision, measures should be taken to ensure that staff members are available to assist when required. Buzzers on doors, for instance, can alert staff to a residents' imminent access to a limited access area, and separate, staff-only power switches can control use of stoves or other appliances.

*Unlimited Access*

Residents can have control over, or access to, some items in or areas of the environment, provided those items or areas have safety precautions designed into them. Examples include timers on stoves or other appliances which automatically turn the power off if a resident forgets, and windows with small openings or locks that allow residents to open them for air but prevent anyone's climbing outside.

# E/H

## Competence in Daily Activities

*Definition:*

The extent to which the environment facilitates or inhibits the residents' ability to carry out daily activities.

Self-esteem and competence are measured by the ability to carry out tasks. A person who is given a difficult task and is able to do it well feels good about him or herself. The same principle holds true for the cognitively impaired (at least for those who have some awareness of their activities). The difference is that such persons are struggling with the most basic activities, for instance dressing, eating, and self-maintenance.

The environment plays a major role in determining the number of activities a person with Alzheimer's disease or a related disorder will be able to complete independently. The environment in which the impaired person lives must provide a variety of supports which become increasingly important as individual abilities decline. As Lawton (1981, 229) writes,

> As individual competence decreases, the environment assumes increasing importance in determining wellbeing. One corollary of this hypothesis is that the low-competent are increasingly sensitive to noxious environments. The opposite, more positive corollary is that a small environmental improvement may produce a disproportionate amount of improvement in affect and behavior in the low-competent individual.

Maximizing the environment's ability to support residents' remaining abilities to carry out activities is a major focus of this book. Complicated mechanisms, or ones requiring several steps for completion will hinder residents' ability to perform tasks on their own. Also, the provision of too many alternatives can make a project more difficult. Both research and popular literature support this theory—that too many choices do not add to, but probably lessen, individual freedom. Toffler (1970), in his book *Future Shock*, theorizes that when the number of options in a decision situation becomes unmanageable, the very freedom associated with this increasing number of alternatives becomes "unfreedom." The key word here is "manageable." What is manageable to one person might be overwhelming to another. The solution is to create an environment which provides some choices (allowing residents to feel in control), but does not offer so many alternatives that it undermines residents' abilities to complete tasks (thereby harming self-esteem).

*Chapter 4*

# Strategies for Environmental Intervention

## Introduction

Once one has become aware of the particular environmental needs of a cognitively impaired population, understands organizational structure and its relation to the creation and running of a special care unit, and has formulated a variety of goals for the special care unit, the actual design process can begin. The design guide that begins with Chapter 5 explores the pertinent environment–behavior interactions for each room or area of the special care unit and presents a variety of design responses to support the needs of the residents and the goals of the unit.

There are two basic approaches to designing an effective physical environment for an ARD unit. These approaches are not mutually exclusive; in fact they can support each other and allow more comprehensive support for a population of residents with different levels of cognitive impairment.

H

## Creating a Homelike Environment

The first approach revolves around providing a homelike environment. This approach to design has been given different names at different times, including "residential" (Koncelik 1976) and "normal" (Robinson et al., 1984). The definition used here is based on the assumption that the person with dementia has led a full and "normal" life until the onset of the disease, and probably lived in a house or apartment/condominium. Therefore, a "homelike" environment is one that resembles, in as many ways as possible, the environment in which the person lived before the onset of the disease. In this respect, the term environment extends beyond physical surroundings to include the social sphere.

A homelike environment adds continuity and familiarity to the lives of the unit's population. This is important because people with dementia do not adjust easily to changes. Therefore, the more the environment resembles "home" the less traumatic it will be for residents to move into a new place and continue their lives. If the environment is familiar, they are more likely to be able to understand and, therefore, cope with it.

There are many ways to create a homelike environment. These can range from simple terminology (referring to a room as the living room, rather than day room or lounge, because most people do not have day rooms in their houses), to allowing and encouraging residents to bring furniture and other personal items when they move to the facility, to using furnishings that might be found in typical noninstitutional homes.

"Homelike" also refers to the size of social groupings. An environment which provides opportunities for groups of 4-8 residents to socialize comfortably is likely to be perceived as more homelike than one that allows socialization only in rooms designed for large groups (Hiatt 1985).

# H

## Prosthetic Support

A living environment designed for the cognitively impaired requires the provision of extra prosthetic supports. (Prosthetics are devices or elements which provide additional functional support to compensate for limited physical or other capabilities.) This additional functional support is usually accomplished by providing added information about the environment (way-finding cues, assistance in activities of daily living); it can also however, include decreasing information (for instance, camouflaging a door to a utility closet).

Prosthetics are found everywhere, not just in institutions. A crutch is a prosthetic device, as are railings in stairwells. Signs, from highway exit signs to "you are here" directional signs, are prosthetic devices, providing added information about the environment. But prosthetics are especially important to the cognitively impaired population, which has diminished ability to remember even the most basic things. For such persons, trying to find the dining room may be as hard after months or years of living in a facility as it was the very first day, *because they can't remember*. The creation of a prosthetic environment can allow all but the most severely impaired residents much more control over their physical environment, and, therefore, more functional independence.

## Combining Physical and Social Prostheses

It must be remembered that most ARD patients will regress beyond the point at which physical prosthetics will provide enough support. These residents will, at some point, require a social support system to help them complete most everyday tasks (i.e., finding the dining room, dressing, eating). It might be possible, for a while, to combine physical and social prosthetics to help the resident maintain a degree of control and self-sufficiency. An example would be a staff member reminding a resident to go to the the toilet, and indicating that the toilet room is bright yellow and has the canopy over the door. With that much direction, the resident might be able to find the way alone. The direct care staff usually provides much of this social support, although other residents might also be able to help. For example, pairing up a resident who cannot find the bathroom with one who can could be beneficial to both.

## Justifying the Costs of Specialized Unit Design

In light of the rising costs of medical and nursing home care, facilities are finding it increasingly difficult to justify spending money to enhance the physical environment. But short-term costs should be weighed against long-term benefits and gains. An appropriately designed environment can make management of cognitively impaired residents much easier and more pleasant for staff. This, in turn, can increase job satisfaction and morale, thus decreasing burnout and costly staff turnover. In addition, many useful design alterations cost little, or can be done as part of a yearly maintenance schedule, if properly planned.

There is some evidence to suggest that a more attractive physical environment encourages families of residents to visit more frequently (Lawton, et al. 1984; personal interviews with several unit directors). This only stands to reason; an environment that is depressing and further diminishes the decreasing capabilities of ARD victims only reminds families of the terrible toll of their relatives' disease. A supportive physical and social environment conveys the message that, while the end result might be the same (total dependence and death), the intermediate stages and day-to-day life can be made more comfortable and pleasant (Lawton 1981).

Equally important, however, are the immeasurable costs of a poorly designed environment, and the benefits of a therapeutically supportive environment, for residents, staff, and families. While there is no cure or effective treatment for these degenerative dementias, quality of life can be enhanced, allowing the residents to maintain their self-respect and dignity, and leave staff and families knowing they've done the best they can under very difficult conditions (Lawton 1981).

# Part II

## Designing
## the Solution

*Chapter 5*

# Basic Design Issues

## Behavioral Considerations

Due to their cognitive impairments, residents with dementia do not see or understand the environment in the same way as cognitively intact persons do. Therefore, they might use and manipulate the environment in ways other than originally intended. For the same reason, people with Alzheimer's disease and related disorders might not comprehend danger in a situation when they encounter it. They might try to cover up mistakes and unwittingly cause even more damage.

*Design Response*

An environment which is more familiar or homelike is less likely to be confusing to the person with dementia by not creating new situations with which residents are unable to deal. There are, however, many potential hazards in even the most residential environments. Several areas, architectural elements, and environmental attributes need to be considered carefully. They fall into two basic categories: those which compensate for physical impairments and those that are necessary because of cognitive impairments.

37

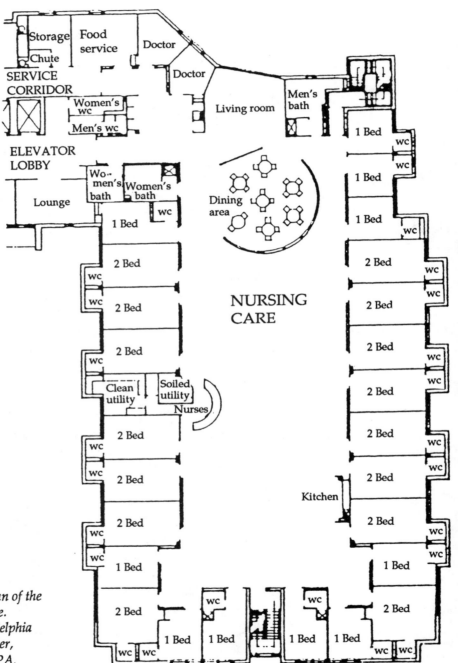

*Figure 5-1* Plan of the
Weiss Institute.
Source: Philadelphia
Geriatric Center,
Philadelphia, PA.

*Spatial Adjacencies*     Two different floor plan schemata have been developed specifically to counter the known deficits of the cognitively impaired elderly population. The Weiss Institute can be described as a pavilion plan (see Figure 5-1). It was first developed by psychologist H. Osmond, architect Kiyoshi Izumi, and the staff at the Philadelphia Geriatric Center. The organizing principle of the Weiss Institute is the widened hallway. The rooms (40 beds in this example) are distributed around an open central space, an arrangement that is "intended to diminish the effects of disorientation and memory loss by giving residents an almost complete view of the area from anywhere in the space" (Liebowitz et al., 1979, 59) The dining room area is set off by a low rail and change in floor color (see Figure 10-4). The nursing station is a large open counter projecting into the central space to allow direct surveillance of all areas.

Lawton and his colleagues have done extensive evaluations of the Weiss Institute, and the results indicate that residents derive distinct benefits from this unique, prosthetic environment. Several measures of positive resident behaviors increased (maximum angle of gaze, increased time spent in "social" spaces, more participation in enriching activities, etc.), while the incidence of pathological behaviors decreased. For further evaluation of the Weiss Institute, the reader is referred to Leibowitz, et al. (1979), Lawton (1981), and Lawton et al. (1984).

A second scheme has recently been developed independently by two architectural firms: Oudens & Knoop in Washington, D.C. and Stevens and Wilkinson in Atlanta, Georgia (see Figures 5-2 and 5-3). Both firms' strategies are new enough that there has been no opportunity to evaluate them in built form; therefore an examination of the plans will have to suffice. Both are based primarily on clustering bedrooms around the central living areas. The Stevens and Wilkinson scheme—that they call a butterfly plan—has two groups or clusters (12-13 beds each) of bedrooms around living areas, and a split nursing station to allow direct visual monitoring by staff members.

*Figure 5-2 Plan of John Douglas French Center for Alzheimer's Disease. Source: John Douglas French Center for Alzheimer's Disease, Los Alamitos, CA. Stevens and Wilkinson, architects.*

1. Patient Room, 1 bed
2. Patient Room, 2 beds
3. Activities
4. Dining
5. Bath

6. Nurses' Station
7. Reception
8. Kitchen
9. Physical Therapy
10. Courtyard

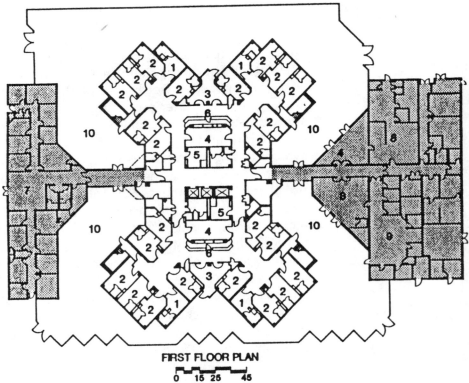

FIRST FLOOR PLAN

0   15  25      45

The Oudens & Knoop plan is similar to Stevens and Wilkinson's but the clusters of rooms (12 beds each) are more separate. Each cluster is given its own identity with a visually distinctive front porch suitable for informal gatherings of residents. The nursing station has clear visual access to the central area, and the dining area has been broken up into two smaller areas. This unit also has direct access to a courtyard for the residents.

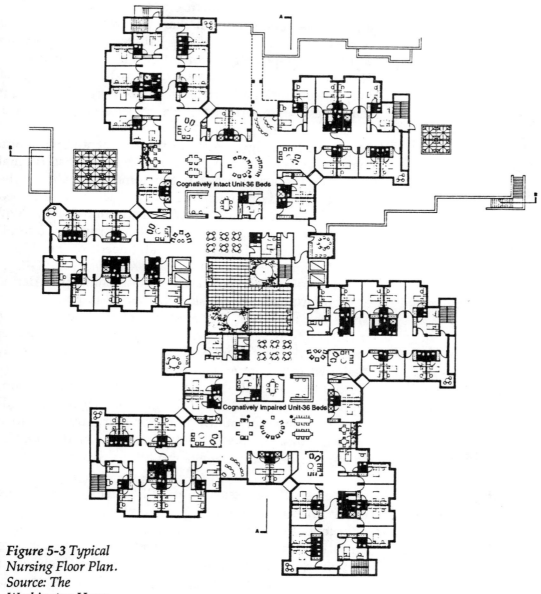

*Figure 5-3 Typical Nursing Floor Plan. Source: The Washington Home, Washington, D.C., Oudens & Knoop, architects.*

The clustering of rooms around central living spaces is a more residential pattern than the traditional nursing home design, in which the long hallway is the organizing principle. Integrating a front porch or other distinctive elements (greenhouse, aviary, etc.) into the unit design not only helps residents identify their own clusters, but reinforces the important distinction between public areas (living and dining rooms) and private (bedrooms and bathrooms) (see Figure 7-2). The prominent nursing station may allow easy surveillance, but add to the institutional character, thereby decreasing the homelike quality of the unit. It is hoped that when the two projects just described are built, the designers and/or institutional staffs will carry out thorough evaluations to further overall understanding of the environmental needs of the elderly with dementia.

The design of the physical environment helps to define a "comfortable" group size for social interaction and organized activities. The evidence clearly points to the preferability of smaller groups (4–8 people) over larger groups of 12–30. If a unit being set up in a facility is already designed to accommodate a relatively large number of residents, several smaller activity/therapy rooms (approximately 150–250 sq. ft.) should be created to provide more congenial surroundings for smaller group activities. Each of these rooms should be somewhat different in character (see Chapter 9, Shared Living Spaces).

# H

## Limiting Access

It is usually necessary on an ARD unit to limit residents' access to certain areas: storage closets for cleaning supplies or potentially hazardous equipment, staff and medication areas, other areas of the facility, and even outdoor spaces. However, residents accustomed to moving freely about their own homes and neighborhoods might resent or be frustrated by such restrictions, and display angry or disruptive behavior. There are a number of ways to decrease the agitation felt by residents at being "locked out" of an area, while still effectively keeping hazardous areas secure. Doors and door handles can be camouflaged (painted to

*Figure 5-4*
*Inconspicuous Lock.*

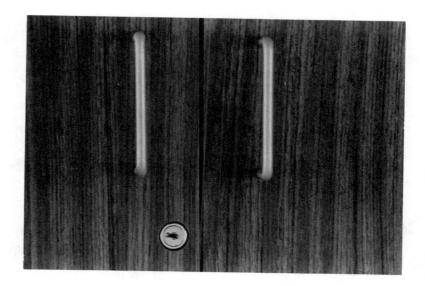

match the surrounding walls), or covered with magnetic boxes which fit over the door handle, but are too secure for the older person to remove. Another possibility is childproof knobs, which require special pressure to open the door. If a lock is necessary, it should be small and inconspicuous (see Figure 5-4).

Access can also be limited by hiding (visually) an opening mechanism. The Philadelphia Geriatric Center employs an excellent example: entry to and exit from the unit requires pressing two buttons, which are on the outside of a pole and far enough apart to be difficult for the older person to reach simultaneously.

The designer might also make entering an area a multistage process. Combination buzzer locks work on this principle, requiring the user to remember a sequence of numbers.

A recent pilot study suggests that there might be even more cost-effective ways of discouraging resident access to certain areas. Hussian and Brown (1987) were able to decrease the number of times residents reached the end of a hall (containing a door which led off the unit) by 55–70% simply by putting rows of masking tape on the floor. The perceptual problems experienced by the ARD population

*Figure 5-5* Entry Gate to the Weiss Institute at the Philadelphia Geriatric Center. Source: Philadelphia Geriatric Center, Philadelphia, PA. Photograph by Harry Finberg. (Reprinted by permission.)

led some of the residents to view these lines on the floor as a barrier. It should be noted that this solution was not effective with all residents, but produced significant improvement at very low cost (see Figure 5-5).

**E**

*Lighting*

Elderly people need 2–3 times more light that do younger people, but are more sensitive to glare. Their eyes do not adjust to contrasts as easily and quickly; therefore, thresholds between spaces with different lighting are potentially hazardous. Direct sunlight causes glare and design should compensate for its effects. Designers must be aware that daylight will reflect off any surface, especially a shiny one, and cause discomfort. Therefore use of matte surfaces is suggested, especially near windows. Indirect light can often provide the most even illumination of a space; a combination of fluorescent and incandescent lighting gives the best quality. Installing a dimmer (which can be turned down at night) on lights in shared living spaces will help indicate that evening is drawing near. This an be especially useful if there are no windows in these areas and therefore no time cues from natural light.

**E**

*Visual Contrasts*

Increasing the contrast between objects (furniture) and the background (walls, floors), or between floors and walls will increase residents' ability to distinguish objects in the environment. A dark wall which meets a lighter floor, or the use of a darker baseboard when both the floor and the wall are light, is suggested. Lack of such contrasts will lead to more accidents, and increase residents' agitation because they will be less able to understand their environment.

**E**

*Furniture*

All furniture in a special care unit should be sturdy, so that residents who need to lean against a piece for support can do so without fear of the chair (or whatever) giving way under them. Also, such relatively lightweight items as lamps should be fastened (for instance, to tables) so they will not fall. There should be no rough edges or frayed fabric. Chairs and tables in a variety of complementary styles, colors, and patterns are more residential than an array of identical pieces, not to mention more considerate of residents' individual preferences. For example, some people find recliner chairs very comfortable for a nap, while some like rockers to help them use up excess energy. All chairs should have arms which extend to the front edge of the seat to aid in standing up. All chairs and tables should have rounded edges.

**H**

*Windows*

In order to enhance residents' feelings of control, they should be able to open windows whenever possible. However, the openings must be too small for a resident to climb through. If existing windows have large openings, locks that limit the amount the windows can be opened can be easily installed (see Figure 5-6).

**E**

*Floors*

All floor surfaces need to be nonskid. Patterns or changes of color on the floor should be avoided, since residents might see them as changes of level. Highly reflective flooring is not advised, since it will cause problems with glare.

**E**

*Carpet*

Carpet can make a unit appear more homelike, and acts to absorb unnecessary noises. There are a number of good antibacterial, stain resistant carpet materials, especially designed for health care use, on the market. Be sure there are no frayed edges or loose strings for the residents to pull or trip over. There are modular carpet tiles available which are designed to be picked up, cleaned, and easily replaced. For this to be successful, initial installation must be very precise. Carpet which is solution dyed is much more resistant to staining, and can withstand a spill of straight bleach without discoloring. Throw rugs should be used with extreme caution; they can cause accidents if they slip. Throw rugs, like patterned tile, also can look like a change in level to the residents, who will try to step over them, creating another potential hazard.

*Figure 5-6 Window.*

### Walls

There is no empirical evidence to support the use of solid over patterned wall coverings, or vice versa. Both types have been used successfully. In general, patterns are more homelike, but bold designs can be overstimulating. Other patterns might look so real that residents will want to pick at them. Solid colors are often more institutional, but can provide an effective background for more interesting wall hangings.

A designer might want to compromise between solid and patterned walls by using a stenciled border pattern. A wide variety of such borders are available; these materials usually do not have to be Class A fire-rated because they cover less than 10% of the wall (check local fire codes). Stenciled border patterns provide some visual interest without too much stimulation.

If noise is a problem, there are a number of acoustical wall carpets available. When used on the lower part of the wall they will also protect against marks from wheelchairs and carts. Another product to consider is a new, heavy-duty paintlike substance which is extremely resistant to scratches and marks.

## E
### Railings

Railings in hallways are required by code. They are used by both mobile residents, for support, and wheelchair-bound residents, to help propel them down the hall. Therefore, railings should be designed for easy access to both groups. In general, railings are about 2 inches in diameter, and mounted 32 inches from the floor. Designers should consider adding another railing at 26 inches for wheelchair-bound residents. Because wheelchair traffic tends to scuff up the wall, carpet or heavy-duty paint on the lower half of the wall may be advisable.

## H
### Wall Sockets

There should be a plug in every unused electrical wall socket. Residents, not remembering what the sockets are for, might "explore" them and be shocked.

### Wall Guards

Guards at corners will protect walls against damage by carts and wheelchairs. Some male residents might urinate in corners, so inside corner guards should also be considered.

### Plants

While live plants are a nice, and homelike, addition to an ARD unit, care should be taken that none of the foliage is poisonous or harmful if ingested.

# Chapter 6

# Bedrooms

## Way-finding/Orientation

*Definition:*

The process by which the environment helps a person derive cues and information to aid in navigation from a point through space to a desired location.

*Behavioral Considerations*

The ability to locate one's room independently increases self-sufficiency and therefore self-esteem. People with Alzheimer's are progressively less able to remember the location of their own bedrooms or distinguish their rooms from those of other residents. Wandering into others' bedrooms can increase anxiety and agitation and/or lead to "borrowing" objects from the unfamiliar room.

*Design Response*

Unless a unit is very small (6–8 residents), it is unlikely that the location and arrangement of the bedrooms is going to be strongly reminiscent of residential patterns. The cluster plan, discussed in Chapter 5 in which bedrooms are grouped in clusters of 6–8, might be one of the more manageable arrangements, making it easier for residents to distinguish their own rooms than do the traditional single-/or double-loaded corridor plans. Some residents might still need some assistance identifying "their" clusters, but the theory is that once a resident enters the correct cluster, there are fewer bedrooms to choose from. If a cluster arrangement is not possible or feasible, prosthetic and social supports become especially important in providing residents opportunities to maintain independence by finding their own rooms.

One of the main environmental characteristics which helps residents find their own rooms is the visual distinctiveness of the rooms and their entries. There are a number of ways to increase visual distinctiveness.

E

**Color.** Some people with dementia retain the ability to recognize and attach importance to colors long into the course of the disease. Colors should be clear and bright. In a study by Alvermann (1979) a group of elderly residents preferred warmer colors (reds, yellows, oranges, browns) over cooler shades (blues and greens). It is helpful to have the residents decide which color(s) they like best and want in their surroundings. Those who do understand direct questions about color preferences can be given a variety of colored items (crayons, markers, paint chips, colored paper), then observed to see which ones they use most often (Roach 1985).

Once a color scheme has been chosen, it can serve as the basis for a system of location cues for residents. For some, a wristband color-coded to match their room will provide a needed reminder. Also, brightly contrasting colors on the door, door frame, or room identification sign, or a bold accent stripe inside the room, can help a resident find the way to the correct quarters.

Evidence suggests that most ARD victims will eventually lose the ability to recognize colors. Therefore, it is suggested that colors be used only in conjunction with other types of cues.

E/H

**Signage.** Room identification signs should be large, with dark letters on a light background. Room numbers alone will usually not be very helpful, but some residents will be able to locate their rooms if their names are on the doors. Residents will try to remove number or name bars; such

*Figure 6-1* Room
Identification—Use of
Photographs in
Signage. Source:
Northvies Home for
Mental Health,
Waukesha, WI.
(Reprinted by
permission.)

SIDNEY JACOBSON

signs should be secured, either to a frame or to the door or wall. Signs can also be used to provide additional memory cues (see sections on personal identification and personal mementos).

E

**Personal Identification.** Many residents respond to pictures of themselves, some to recent pictures, others to pictures of themselves at an earlier time. Staff should determine if each resident recognizes a current picture or one from an earlier period—preferably one which has some personal significance. Engagement, wedding, and birthday photographs are often good choices; family members often can provide such pictures. If a resident responds to a picture, it should be placed in an easily visible location, either on the room sign or on the door, to serve as an orientation cue (see Figure 6-1).

*Figure 6-2 Room Identification—Use of Personal Mementos. Source: Wesley Hall, Chelsea Methodist Home, Chelsea, MI, and Institute of Gerontology, University of Michigan, Ann Arbor, MI.*

E

**Personal Mementos.** Some residents will not recognize their own picture, be it current or from an earlier time. They might, however, identify with some other picture (their house, a favorite pet, a scenic view, etc.) or object. It might be necessary to work with the family to find the appropriate item. If the person was a florist, consider a dried bouquet or nosegay; for a carpenter, try a picture of a toolbox with tools (see Figure 6-2).

Some residents will recognize something they have made, perhaps a drawing done in an art therapy group. Like nameplates and photographs, mementos should be placed in a visible location, and secured firmly so others will not try to remove them. Lockable, well-lit shelves will provide the opportunity for residents to display personal mementos safely, not only providing additional orientation cues, but adding visual interest to the area (see Figure 6-3).

E/H

*Placement of Cues*

All cues should be placed so that the residents can see them. If there are residents confined to wheelchairs, signs should be no higher that 40–44 inches from the floor. Staff

*Figure 6-3 Room Identification—Use of Display Shelves. Source: Corinne Dolan Alzheimer's Center, Hether Hill, Chardon OH, Taliesin Associated Architects.*

should also be aware of the particular visual patterns of individual residents—especially those having trouble finding their rooms. Some residents might walk the hall and never look into the rooms, so signs or pictures on an open bedroom door will not be seen. Others may look only at objects at railing height, and others only at the floor. Whatever is necessary to create a visually distinctive bedroom door and entry which the residents will attend to should be done, even if it means putting the cue at the bottom of the door. A sign that is perpendicular to the wall will provide more information to a person down the hall than one that is flush.

## Social Supports

Some residents will not respond to any visual environmental cues, no matter how distinctive. Such persons might not be able to make the connection between the cues and the fact that the cues indicate their room, or they might simply forget what they are looking for. Social support of way-finding should begin with gentle reminders of what the person should look for: point to the colored wristband; or ask about the picture of the grandchildren; or, if, for instance, there are flowers on the bedroom door, talk about what a talented florist the resident was. These measures might be enough to jog the person's memory. Still, some resident might need to be led to their rooms. A roommate or other resident might be able to function as a guide, which might be seen as less of a loss of control than being led by a staff member. This "buddy system" can also have added benefits for more capable residents, giving their lives more purpose (Cox 1985).

## Personalization

*Definition:*

The degree to which the environment encourages or discourages a resident's ability to have control over the placement and arrangement of personal effects.

*Behavioral Considerations*

Personalization of the bedroom will add continuity to the life of a person moving into a facility by acknowledging the past instead of denying it. Also, increased familiarity with the environment, resulting from the presence of personal effects, can decrease the anxiety often felt by cognitively impaired persons moving to an institution. Personalization creates an opportunity for residents to have control over their immediate surroundings. This territoriality is a basic human need and does not disappear or lessen when one moves into an institution.

*Design Response*

The bedroom is usually the most personal area of a house. It is where persons can arrange the furniture and decorations according to their own wishes (as opposed to the living areas, in which sociocultural mores are followed more closely). This pattern should continue to be true when a person moves to an institution.

It is especially important for a new resident to feel comfortable on the unit. The move to an institution is traumatic for anyone, but is especially so for the confused, cognitively impaired person. There has been extensive research on the effects of relocation on elderly persons (Bourestom and Pastalan 1981; Schulz and Alderman 1973; Turner et al., 1972). The results of several studies indicate that negative effects are much higher as a function of marked differences between pre- and postrelocation environments (i.e., from home to institution) (Aldrich and Mendkoff 1963; Miller and Lieberman 1965). One way to decrease the negative effects of such a move is to let the resident and family participate in decorating the bedroom.

**Walls.** Institutions should choose a color scheme which provides three or four personal decorating alternatives. Either paint or wallpaper is acceptable, but wallpaper will be more expensive in the long run. Whichever is used, the surface should be able to accommodate hanging pictures and cards without showing damage. The walls do not necessarily need to be recovered for every new resident, but when it is time to repaint or repaper, ask residents and families to state their preferences.

**Floor.** Carpeting can be put into the bedrooms if the occupants have not regressed to the point of frequent, uncontrollable incontinence. If carpeting is to be put into the bedrooms, allow the residents to choose among several colors. This might be appropriate only for a newly designed or renovated unit; it is prohibitively expensive to provide such choices for each new resident. Throw rugs are not suggested (see Chapter 5).

**Windows and Curtains.** Unequal division of territory or space often occurs in semiprivate rooms, especially those with only one window. Whenever possible, residents should have equal amounts of space and equal access to the window(s). It is a simple matter, when ordering curtains, to order sets in three or four complementary colors and patterns, and to order a few extra. This allows new residents to make decorating decisions based on preference, thereby allowing them to exercise control over their environment.

E

**Bedspreads and bed curtains.** The policy here should be the same as for curtains. Personal choice can be enhanced further by allowing each resident to bring a quilt or spread from home. Fire regulations must, of course, be checked. If all fabrics *must* be fire-rated, and a resident is truly attached to a quilt, it should be possible for the family to have it fire-proofed.

E

**Furniture.** Policy on residents bringing in their own furniture varies among institutions. In general, it is advantageous to allow residents to bring with them at least one piece—perhaps a chair or dresser—to which they are particularly attached. This increases the feeling that the unit is now home. Staff should check to be sure residents' personal furniture is sturdy and in good repair. It is also advantageous to let residents have some control over where their furniture is placed. This might be more difficult in rooms shared by two or three people, but efforts should be made to be as accommodating as possible. In addition to the main lighting for the room, separate lamps for each resident, *which they can turn on and off*, are important. It should be difficult to remove the bulb from bedside lamps; some residents hoard bulbs. Finally, the unit can be made more homelike by avoiding "institutional"-looking furniture. A number of manufacturers now carry residential-looking beds in several different styles. Having a few extra head- and footboards in different styles will increase residents' options, thereby providing more individual control over the environment (see Figure 6-4).

E

**Decorations.** Each resident should be encouraged to bring at least one, if not several, pictures to hang on the bedroom wall. Pictures should be attached firmly (i.e., with screws) so that residents will not try to remove them. Again, residents should be allowed to determine where they want each picture hung.

E

**Display.** Built-in shelves or special nooks encourage residents to personalize their rooms. Glass doors installed over shelves decrease opportunities for residents to "borrow" personal items from other people (see Figure 6-3).

**Figure 6-4** *Example of a Residential Bedroom. Source: Wesley Woods, Atlanta, GA.*

## Safety and Security

*Definition:*

The degree to which the environment is designed to avoid the occurrence of accidents while not inhibiting the ease of locomotion through, and use of, the environment.

*Behavioral Considerations*

Because residents are often in their rooms without supervision, increased safety precautions are necessary to avoid unnecessary accidents. Furthermore, a safe environment encourages residents to be more involved with their immediate surroundings because they aren't as afraid of causing accidents (Andreason 1985).

*Design Response*

In the process of providing a homelike environment over which residents have some control, several important safety issues emerge. A few of these have already been discussed, for instance floor colors or patterns that can cause residents to think there is a change in level, or window openings large enough for residents to climb out. But there are others.

E

**Furniture.** All furniture, especially pieces brought in by residents, should be checked carefully and determined to be in good repair. Any loose threads, holes in the fabric, or cracked wooden joints will undoubtedly be found by the residents and cause problems. For sanitary reasons, vinyl coating of fabric on chairs is recommended. If this is not possible (e.g., on a chair brought in by resident), cushion covers should be easily washable. One way to protect a cushion inside its original cover is to remove the cover, wrap the cushion in a double layer of plastic (garbage bags work), then replace the cover. (Note: Local fire regulations might make it necessary to find another way to protect the cushions.) Fabric protector spray can also be used to help protect the fabric. As stated before, furniture should also be heavy enough so that it does not slide or move if a resident leans on it for support.

H

**Storage.** Storage space is often limited in residents' rooms. Underbed storage units, perhaps equipped with locks, can help avoid overcrowding of closets and shelves (a potentially hazardous situation). This would allow storage of offseason clothes in an out-of-sight location, thereby eliminating unnecessary or undesirable options from the wardrobe.

H

**Locks.** When locks are necessary—on windows (so residents can't climb out or open windows in the winter), in the bathroom, on wardrobes/closets, etc.— inconspicuous locks with "tube keys" should be installed. This will cause less agitation among residents than will combination or padlocks. Locks or other safety devices should be used only when absolutely necessary (see Figure 5-4).

E

**Beds.** Beds should not be equipped with railings that fold down to the floor, because it is easy for residents to get their feet caught in them. If the resident is not likely to fall out of bed, remove the railings altogether. If railings are absolutely necessary, find ones that do not fold down to the floor.

## Activities of Daily Living

*Definition:*

The extent to which the environment facilitates or inhibits the resident's ability to carry out daily activities.

*Behavioral Considerations*

Many self-maintenance and grooming activities occur in the bedroom. The ability to perform these activities for oneself is essential to maintaining self-esteem. Different residents will want to engage in different activities—e.g., some will like cleaning their rooms, while others might never have done that themselves—and the environment should support this diversity.

E/H

*Design Response*

**Dressing.** A homelike environment should have built-in closets and a separate dresser for each resident. Closet doors which open wide to show all of the clothes inside decrease the chances that a resident will forget to put on an article of clothing. Of course, too many choices can be as bad as no choices at all, so only a few outfits should be available at one time for the resident to choose among. Eventually, many residents will become unable to make appropriate decisions about what to wear, or to remember the order in which articles of clothing should go on. There are closet systems available with special hooks in which the clothes to be worn the next day are laid out in the order in which they are to be put on. This can provide the assistance necessary to let some residents continue to dress themselves. Also, labels can help residents remember what is in drawers. When the cognitively impaired person eventually loses the ability to manage any fasteners, staff assistance will be necessary.

E/H

**Grooming.** Easy access to mirrors encourages residents to notice and possibly take pride in their appearance. Every room should have a mirror from which residents can see themselves, from at least the waist up, clearly. This should also be true for wheelchair-bound residents. If necessary, mirrors can be outfitted with hinges so that they tilt to meet the visual needs of a variety of residents. High visibility of and easy access to mirrors increases the likelihood that residents will use them. It is common in residences to have a comb and brush by the mirror; this pattern should be continued in the institution if possible. Hanging one mirror in a shared room above one dresser and none above the other should be avoided, as this can lead to territorial problems. Mirrors should be either above each dresser, over the sink, or by the door, possibly with a shelf for brushes and combs.

E

**Cleaning.** Some persons have established, lifelong patterns of cleaning their rooms. Such routines need not stop upon entering an institution. Capable, willing residents can be in charge of making their beds, putting away clothes, dusting, and sweeping, especially if measures are taken to make those tasks easier. Persons who have not done such chores throughout their lives should not be introduced to new responsibilities on the unit, however, since housekeeping tasks might be too complicated to learn at that point.

Bedmaking can be a difficult task, with many steps to remember. A picture by the bed of the various steps in this process might help to jog the memories of some residents. Wide bedspreads lessen the necessity to tuck in blankets, also making the process easier. A clearly marked hamper for dirty clothes will help residents know where to put clothes that have been worn. (Hampers should be emptied regularly, because other residents may remove clothes from them.) Bedmaking, dusting, and sweeping might need to be prompted by staff. *Assistance* by staff allows residents to feel more competent than if staff members take housekeeping jobs over completely.

E

**Leisure/Activities.** Residents will probably spend some of their free time in their rooms. They should be able to control such activities as opening and closing windows and/or curtains. If residents cannot remember how to open the window or curtains, simple instructions on the wall might be all that is necessary. Mechanisms should be simple. Curtains on rings that simply slide across a rod are easier to manipulate than drapes requiring residents to pull a string to open and close them. Many cognitively impaired residents still enjoy listening to the radio or watching television. If a resident is no longer able to remember how to change radio stations, a staff member should find the one he or she seems to like best (or ask the family about longstanding tastes), and leave the dial there. Television can be more of a problem, because some residents will have delusions about the "little people" on the screen, thinking they are children, or become frightened by the news programs. TV watching needs to be monitored carefully, and discussed with the family if it becomes clear that a television is inappropriate for any given resident.

*Chapter 7*

# Corridors

---

## Way-finding/Orientation

*Definition:*

The process by which the environment helps a person derive cues and information to aid in navigation from a point through space to a desired location.

*Behavioral Considerations*

The ability to see one's goal or desired location from one's present position significantly increases the ability to move independently, thereby increasing self-sufficiency (Weisman, in press). Because residents of ARD units have a decreased ability to remember paths, orienting information/cues must be provided along the way. This is especially important if the goal, or destination, is not visible. Information/cues must also be present at key decision points: wherever two halls meet, or wherever a person must make a decision about which way to go (Weisman, in press; Carpman et al., 1985).

If there are multiple, similarly designed corridors on the unit, residents might confuse them with each other. This can be a factor in the wandering and apparent confusion among ARD residents.

*Design Response*

In many facilities, both older and some newly constructed buildings, all hallways are virtually identical. A variety of techniques can be employed to give each hall a visually distinct character; these include the use of color and patterns, the location and type of artwork, and the location of furniture. Without these added cues, it is unreasonable to expect even mildly confused persons (residents or nonresidents) to be able to orient themselves within the space.

E

**Color.** If there are several halls in the unit, decorating them in different colors can help some residents remember the location of their room or common rooms. Bright, clear, warm colors are preferred (Alverman 1979). Color, when combined with different wall treatments, patterns, or textures will be more effective and/or meaningful to the residents (see signage).

E

**Signage.** Due to the complex nature of an institution, and to the limited mental capacity of the ARD population, signs are often necessary. Both words and graphics should be used; dark words, with letters two to three inches high, and dark graphics on a light background are easiest for elderly persons to distinguish (Carpman et al., 1985). Graphics should be realistic, not abstract. For the dining room, for instance, a picture/graphic of a place setting is a good choice (see Figure 10-6). Signs for living/activity room(s) should include something that is clearly part of the residents' experiences in that room: a picture of a T.V., a comfortable chair, games. Consider testing a selection of intended graphics on the population before deciding which ones to place on the walls.

Artwork, creatively used, can also be a form of signage, conveying important information. If there are several halls or wings of bedrooms, each might be given a theme, i.e., trees and flowers, cars and boats, animals. The theme should be used for all artwork on the hall. The location of thematic artwork or hangings at key decision points (see section on behavioral considerations) can be used effectively to help residents find their way around the unit.

E

**Latent Cues.** There are many ways besides signs to help residents orient themselves within a hallway. If halls are wider than the minimum required width (usually eight feet), part of the room might be brought into the hall (Weisman, in press). Two comfortable chairs by the entrance to the living room will be enough to cue some residents to the location of the living room, and will draw other residents there even though they might not be able to remember that that is the location of the living room. If there are plants, one might be placed outside the door; staff should make sure it is nonpoisonous, or use silk flowers if necessary. Other interesting wall hangings, a quilt for example, can serve as latent cues (see Figure 7-1).

*Figure 7-1 Quilt Used as an Orientation Cue. Source: Family Hospital Nursing Home, Milwaukee, WI.*

*Figure 7-2 Front Porch for Bedroom Cluster. Source: The Washington Home, Washington D.C., Oudens & Knoop, architects.*

E

H

*Wandering*

**Landmarks.** A landmark establishes a clear reference point which allows a person to become oriented within the environment. It should be highly visible and memorable and/or significant. The nurse's station can serve as a landmark, although this is not a particularly homelike element (see Figure 13-1). A bay window with a particularly interesting view and a window seat, a greenhouse, the kitchen, or a grandfather clock can all serve as landmarks (Weisman, in press). One facility has a "front porch" at the entrance to each bedroom wing. Each was designed to be visually distinctive and to act as a semi-private transition space. (See Figure 7-2.)

If the unit is designed so that the key areas are not visible, landmarks can draw residents from one location to another, reducing the number of steps they must remember without aid.

Orientation and way-finding problems are only one possible cause of wandering. As mentioned in Chapter 1 the environment should allow for safe wandering without increasing residents' anxiety or risk by leading them into dead-end situations. There are several potential solutions to this problem, depending on the layout of the unit.

In a more traditional facility, a single, centrally located shared living space means that the wanderer will probably be walking up and down halls which end in dead-ends. Watching residents will reveal if there is a typical wandering path; if so, a pleasant shared living room might be set up at each end of the path. In this way, the wanderer is walking between rooms or places—not just down dead-end hallways. In addition, any ongoing activities in these rooms might encourage the person to join in with other residents instead of walking the halls alone. (See Figure 7-3.)

Another response to wandering lies in creating an "endless corridor" or racetrack in which the wanderer never comes to the end of the hall. Such a plan can be used to create several paths, allowing the wanderer more choices of routes. Staff at several facilities using this type of plan feel that the habitual wanderer is less frustrated by this type of plan. (See Figure 7-4.)

*Figure 7-3 Living Rooms at Ends of Wandering Path. Source: Rocky Knoll, Plymouth, WI.*

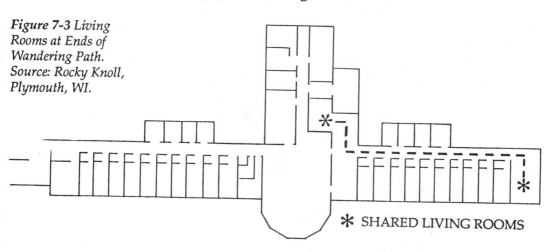

✱ SHARED LIVING ROOMS

**Figure 7-4** *Endless Corridor. Source: Corinne Dolan Alzheimer's Center Healther Hill, Chardon, OH, Taliesin Associated Architects.*

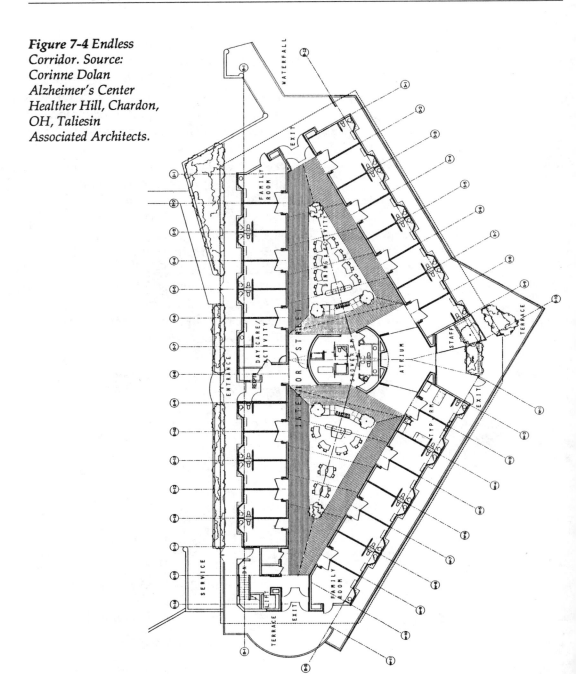

*Figure 7-5 Interactive Wall Art. Source: Iowa Veterans Home, Iowa City, IA.*

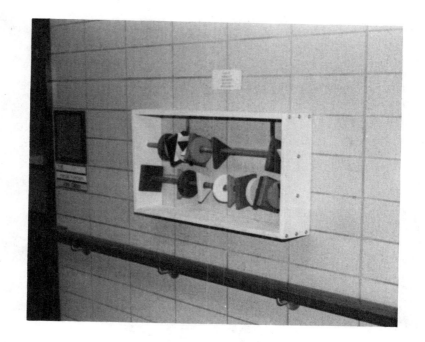

In addition to access to the living rooms, the provision of interactive wall art or textured scenes on the walls can provide effective distraction for wandering residents. (See Figures 7-5 and 7-6.)

## Privacy and Socialization

*Definition:*

The degree to which the environment inhibits or facilitates opportunities for a person to control amounts of privacy and social contact with other people.

*Behavioral Considerations*

Residents tend to congregate around activity nodes; it is necessary to provide space for such gatherings so they do not impede traffic flow. In addition, places should be available for those people who prefer to watch ongoing activities "privately," without having to be around other people.

*Figure 7-6* Tactile
Wall Hangings.
Source: Heather Hill,
Chardon, OH.
Photograph by Joan
Lindsay.

Casual conversations are more likely to occur in corridors where there is space for two or three people to gather out of the flow of traffic than in corridors where people must stand in the middle of the hall to talk (Weisman, in press).

E

*Design Response*

**Artwork.** Pictures of residents can be used to increase social interaction in the halls. Polaroid pictures of the residents engaged in special activities (i.e., pizza night, a birthday party, Christmas) can be put together in a poster format. Many residents enjoy looking at these pictures. (See Figure 7-7.)

If there is someone on the staff, or a resident's family member, who is a good photographer, enlarged and framed pictures of the residents can also be very nice. Pictures of residents have the added benefit of making the unit more of a "family."

*Figure 7-7 Recent Activities Board.*

*Figure 7-8 Resident of the Month Display. Source: Shorehaven Home, Oconomowoc, WI.*

Some facilities have "resident of the month" displays, with several pictures (current and older) and some information about job, hobbies, family, etc. on a board. This can be used effectively in reminiscence therapy. It can also provide a casual gathering spot for residents, bringing them together and giving them something to talk about. Bulletin boards, calendars, and current event boards should be in public areas. (See Figure 7-8.)

If there is a problem with residents picking at things on the display boards, displays can be covered with a sheet of lucite which is built into a frame. This can be attached to the

*Figure 7-9 Lucite Protective Frame.*

board on hinges so the display is easy to change, but will keep residents from having access to the display itself (see Figure 7-9).

Design should make it as easy as possible for residents to tell the difference between public and private halls. Different types of artwork should be used on the different types of halls.

E

**Nooks.** The creation and location of nooks along hallways can allow residents to watch ongoing activities, for example, the routine at the nurse's station, or particularly pleasant outside views. If nooks vary in size and location, they allow residents to choose between socializing with others or having time by themselves (Weisman, in press).

Staff and families can reinforce the use of nooks by spending time with residents there. If such places are pleasant, interesting or active, they are more,likely to be used frequently. (See Figures 7-10 and 7-11.)

*Figure 7-10 Seating
Nook, Before Changes.
Source: Northview
Home for Mental
Health, Waukesha, WI.*

E

**Furniture.** In some facilities, shared living spaces are almost extensions of the halls, with no doorways to the rooms. If this is the case, and hallways are wider than the minimum width, some of the furniture should be moved into the hall.

*Figure 7-11* *Seating*
*Nook, After Changes.*
*Source: Northview*
*Home for Mental*
*Health, Waukesha, WI.*

Not only does this help orient residents, it claims the hall
as public, not private, space. This arrangement should not
be used in bedroom (private) halls.

# Chapter 8

# Hygiene Facilities

## Way-finding/Orientation

*Definition:*

The process by which the environment helps a person derive cues and information to aid in navigation from a point through space to a desired location

*Behavioral Considerations*

Toileting is normally a very private activity. Increased ability to locate the toilet rooms independently gives residents more of a feeling of self-sufficiency. It can also decrease the number of accidents.

Toilets which are visible from and easily accessible to the bedroom will remind residents to use the bathroom more frequently than will bathrooms which are not as visible (e.g., shared facilities). If there are shared bathrooms, there should be a clear distinction between the men's room and the women's room or residents will enter the wrong room, especially if the two facilities are adjacent.

*Design Response*

Whenever possible, each bedroom, or at the most two rooms, should be equipped with a toilet and sink. This is a typical pattern in residences, in which the master bedroom has a bathroom adjacent. If the door is not visually distinctive in its own right, a sign might be necessary to remind residents of the bathroom's location.

When private facilities are not possible, it is even more important to make the toilet rooms clearly visible. Whenever possible, toilet rooms should be located adjacent to shared living areas. This increased proximity will remind residents to use the toilets frequently and will make it easier for staff to direct residents there.

E/H

**Visibility/Distinctiveness.** A number of techniques can increase the visibility of bathrooms. Painting the door a bright color and increasing the contrast between the door frame and the wall are two possibilities. Giving the door a different treatment from all other doors in the area is another useful technique. A fabric canopy over the door not only differentiates the bathroom from other rooms, but also increases the visibility of the bathroom from down the hall because it is three-dimensional and extends into the hallway (see Figure 8-1).

*Figure 8-1 Canopy Used to Increase Visual Distinctiveness of Shared Hygiene Facilities. Source: Wesley Hall, Chelsea Methodist Home, Chelsea, MI, and Institute of Gerontology, University of Michigan, Ann Arbor, MI.*

H

**Graphics.** The use of graphics on toilet room doors can also increase way-finding abilities (Weisman, in press). Several graphics should be tested on the population first to see which are most effective. The traditional (international) graphic of the man in pants and the woman in a dress is one possibility, although there is some evidence that this does not work very well. Other alternatives include a picture of a toilet and old-fashioned pictures of a man and woman. Positioning the sign so that it is visible from down the hall will provide more assistance to the confused resident.

H

**Continuity.** The color, pattern, and/or graphic symbolism used outside the bathroom door should be carried inside the room to increase identification. New fixtures (sinks, toilets, partitions) should be color-coordinated with the entrance. If a bright color has been chosen for the door, and it is too intense for the walls inside, the stalls can be painted in the same color and a less intense shade used for the walls. Tile patterns used inside the toilet room can also be brought outside the door.

**Other Cues.** Toileting often occurs after meals. If residents have trouble locating the toilets from the dining room, consider adding a line on the wall (either by the railing or at eye level) from the dining room to the toilet rooms. Then residents need to remember only to follow the line instead of remembering to go to the end of the hall, turn right, and find the third door on the left. Care should be taken not to put the line on the floor, because residents with decreased visual acuity might think this is a change in floor level.

*Social Supports*

Even with physical orientation aids, some residents will not be able to locate bathrooms on their own, or will not remember that they are to use these rooms. Increased visual distinctiveness can make giving directions to the bathroom easier. At some point, though, most residents will need to be led to the toilet rooms.

## Activities of Daily Living

*Definition:*

The extent to which the environment facilitates or inhibits the resident's ability to carry out daily living activities.

*Behavioral Considerations*

Group bath and toilet rooms are often places of high resident anxiety and agitation. These high agitation levels can decrease the basic functional level of the residents.

Activities of daily living (ADLs) are considered the most basic and private functions. Loss of ability in this area can be particularly distressing to the person with dementia, while retaining the capacity to perform ADLs can increase the residents' feelings of dignity.

*Design Response*

Private or semiprivate toilet facilities allow residents to have their own soap, brush, towel, and toothbrush handy and visible at all times, encouraging independent use of those items.

There is no empirical data to support the use of showers over tubs. Staff in different facilities with different populations have found both to be effective in providing dignified bathing. It is suggested that both be available on the unit for residents who have a clear preference for one over the other. The shower stall should be large enough to allow staff members to assist those residents who require aid. Bathtubs, be they the traditional residential style or hydrotherapy units, should have clear access on at least two (preferably three) sides. There are a number of new tubs on the market which eliminate the need to lift the user over the side, a particularly frightening experience for many residents. There is no empirical evidence yet to indicate which of these tubs works best.

Most companies will bring a sample tub to the facility for inspection. It should be examined, not only by staff, but also by a resident or two, to see how difficult it is to get them into the tub.

E

**Sinks.** Most facilities have at least a sink in each bedroom. In the rooms, and/or in shared bathrooms, all hot water taps should be color-coded to remind residents which is for hot and which for cold water. Also be sure that the water temperature is controlled so residents cannot burn themselves on water that is too hot. A high contrast between the colors of the sink and the counter top (if there is one) will help residents.

E

**Storage of personal items.** If bathrooms are shared, each resident should have a separate cabinet in which to keep personal items. Ideally, residents should have access to their cabinets at all times, but locks might be necessary to deter "borrowing" by others. It might also be necessary for staff to keep all toothbrushes, washcloths and/or brushes, and towels, handing them to each resident at the appropriate times.

E

**Accessibility.** Toilet stalls must be not only handicapped accessible, but also large enough to allow at least one staff person to enter and assist residents who need help. Wall-mounted toilets make it easier to clean the floor around the toilet than do floor-mounted styles.

E

**Surfaces.** Tiles and hard surfaces are often considered necessary for sanitary reasons, but they reflect noise, and high sound levels have been identified as one of the factors leading to increased agitation in bath and toilet rooms. Generous use of sound-absorbing material can help alleviate this problem, as can padded sheet vinyl flooring which, in addition to being easy to care for, absorbs sounds, is softer, and can help prevent injury in case of falls.

Floor drains are essential in all areas where there is water: shower and tub rooms, shared toilet rooms, and private toilet rooms. Drains must have very small openings so residents aren't tempted to put small objects through the grills.

*Chapter 9*

# Shared Living Spaces

---

## Privacy and Socialization

*Definition:*
The extent to which the environment facilitates or inhibits opportunities for residents to control amounts of privacy and social contact between people.

*Behavioral Considerations*
People are more likely to interact with others when seating arrangements are sociopetal (grouped together to encourage social interactions) (Holahan 1972; Holahan and Seagert 1973). Research also indicates that greater opportunities for privacy increase levels of social interaction (Lawton et al., 1970) A proper balance of activities and choices is vital. Environments which provide either too much or not enough stimulation can increase the occurrence of null behavior (see Chapter 4), which can decrease levels of competence (Lawton and Nahemow 1973).

*Design Response*
At one level, even the terminology used to label areas can make a difference to the cognitively impaired population. Referring to shared living space as the "living room" helps residents understand the space and its use. To make this work, however, the room must also fit into their expectations of what a living room is (see Figure 9-1).

83

*Figure 9-1* Living Room. *Source: Wesley Hall, Chelsea Methodist Home, Chelsea, MI, and Institute of Gerontology.*

A major portion of the resident's day is usually spent in shared living areas, either for formal activities and therapies, or during unscheduled freetime. The goal of the design of the living room(s) should be to encourage residents to engage in group activities while allowing opportunities to be alone or watch others engaged in activities. This choice allows residents some measure of control over their lives. (See Figure 9-2.)

**Location.** The ability of the staff to have direct visual access to shared living spaces is usually a high priority in planning the location of common areas. Consequently, the day room is usually centrally located and adjacent to the nursing station. This has the advantage of allowing staff to observe the residents and activities from their post. It has several disadvantages, however. Residents often congregate around the nursing station because this is typically the center of activity. This can cause problems if the hallway or open space is not large enough to accommodate both gathered residents and the normal traffic flow. Another disadvantage of the single, centrally located living room is that it does not provide as many opportunities for wanderers

*Figure 9-2 Corridor and Dining Room. Source: Corinne Dolan Alzheimer's Center, Heather Hill, Chardon, OH, Taliesin Associated Architects.*

to join ongoing activities as does a plan which has several smaller, remote, shared living rooms.

When possible, several smaller activity/therapy rooms should be provided. Residents will be better able to perform tasks in a less overwhelming, less overstimulating environment. Each room should be visually distinctive. One could be a living room, with carpet, comfortable wingback chairs, a rocker, an armchair, and pictures which might stimulate conversation and reminiscence. Another might be the craft room, with tables, lots of storage space for activity supplies, and a sink for washing up.

**Furniture.** Seating should be comfortable and look residential. Plain colored vinyls are still the standard covering in most institutions. For many years this was the only suitable option, especially for a population which often has problems with incontinence. But there are now a large number of pleasant, vinyl-coated, residential-looking fabrics on the market. In addition, this vinyl coating process can be applied to almost any fabric. Chairs should provide good lower back support and have arms that extend all the way to the front of the seat. (See Chapter 6 for more detail about seating.)

Chairs and tables should be arranged in small clusters, with chairs at right angles to each other. Tables with lamps will not only make the room appear more residential, but also will make the lighting quality more pleasant. (See Chapter 5 for more detail about lamps.)

E

**Group size.** People with dementia are better able to cope with small group activities—4-6 people (Hiatt 1983). Some more physical activities, like a balloon toss, can work with 8-10 people. Groups larger than 12 tend to be overstimulating and cause confusion and agitation in residents. In general, common room(s) should be arranged to suit groups between four and eight.

E

**Noise.** Overstimulation from noise is also a major problem in special care units. The healthy, intact younger person can easily screen out undesired background noise, and in fact does so subconsciously. Unit staff, therefore, might not be aware of the cacophony which assails the ears of elderly residents (Jordan 1977; Izumi 1976). Presbycousis is a decrease in upper-range hearing acuity that frequently affects older people. It makes it more difficult to hear conversations in a room with background noise. Generous use of sound-absorbing materials can help: carpet over either the floors or the lower half of the walls, acoustic ceiling tiles, fire proof fabric or carpet wall hangings (notice what airlines are doing with carpet these days). Carpet on the walls can also provide excellent tack-up space which does not show wear and tear. It is important to use wall carpet for hanging; floor carpet will not meet fire codes (see Chapter 6).

**Visual barriers.** The existence of visual barriers between spaces is controversial. Some argue that increased visual access to all areas of the shared living areas will, (1) increase participation in activities because residents can easily see what is going on, (2) increase visual interest/stimulation, thus providing residents with something interesting to watch, and (3) facilitate way-finding by increasing residents' orientation capacity (Lawton et al., 1984; Leibowitz et al. 1979). Others counter by saying that increased visual access, (1) distracts residents, making it harder to keep therapies and group activities together, and (2) causes more visual stimulation than the cognitively impaired person can cope with, thereby increasing confusion and agitation. One possible solution to this problem is the installation of folding partition walls. These can be installed in separate panels, allowing more flexibility; sometimes spaces can be separated totally, and at other times there can be partial barriers. Another solution would be the provision of half-walls, possibly with glass on the upper half. Half-walls differentiate the space while still allowing some visibility between areas. The glass decreases noise transmission between spaces. Half-walls with glass can be equipped with blinds or shades to provide visual separation when desired (see Figure 9-2).

## Personalization

*Definition:*

The degree to which the environment encourages residents' ability to have control over the placement and arrangement of personal effects.

*Behavioral Considerations*

A major portion of most residents' days is spent in the living room or other shared living spaces. Residents will feel more at ease in rooms that are comfortable and familiar. The unit, especially if it has limited access, fundamentally becomes home for the residents. A typical home is not devoid of personal items; therefore the unit should also seek ways to display residents' possessions.

*Design Response*

Residents should be encouraged to bring with them such items as pictures or furniture for the public spaces as well as for their own rooms (Alvermann 1979). Space should be available to store and display or use these items safely.

E

**Furniture.** Placing several residents' favorite chairs in the living room will not only make the room more comfortable, it might help residents maintain some personal identity (see Figure 9-3). If there are territorial problems, that is, if

*Figure 9-3 Residential Furniture in Living Room. Source: Heather Hill, Chardon, OH.*

*Figure 9-4 Framed
Artwork by Residents.
Source: Mt. Carmel,
Waukesha, WI.*

a resident gets upset over other residents sitting in his or
her chair, it might be relocated to the bedroom. If residents
(or families) are unwilling to bring furniture to the unit, or
if furniture is purchased to supplement that brought from
home, unit-owned pieces should look residential, not
institutional. (also see Chapter 5).

E

Artwork. Old or current photographs of residents pictures
or wall hangings from home, or artwork that residents
have done can all be used to make the unit's common areas
more interesting and pleasant (see Figure 9-4). Moreover,
they can make the unit population seem more like a family.
(For more detail, see Chapter 6).

*Chapter 10*

# Dining Room

---

## Activities of Daily Living

*Definition:*

The extent to which the environment facilitates or inhibits the resident's ability to carry out daily living activities.

*Behavioral Considerations*

Mealtimes require high amounts of concentration from residents; they can be one of the most demanding times of the day. Agitation and confusion caused by overstimulation (too many people, too much noise, etc.) can affect concentration and/or cause catastrophic reactions. People develop individual meal time and eating patterns, to which they can be very partial. Continuation of these patterns decreases agitation in a cognitively impaired person. Proper manipulation of the utensils can become increasingly difficult for persons with dementia. This frustration can hinder their desire and capacity to feed themselves (Hiatt 1981; Roach 1985). Loss of ability to feed oneself can be traumatic and seriously decrease feelings of self-worth (Snyder 1984).

*Design Response*

Residents' dining skills and habits are learned early and developed over a lifetime. An institution should try to accommodate as many of these individual patterns as possible.

91

*Figure 10-1 Dining Room Table. Source: Wesley Hall, Chelsea Methodist Home, Chelsea, MI, and Institute of Gerontology, University of Michigan, Ann Arbor MI.*

E/H

**Techniques to Increase Visual Acuity.** It has been suggested (Hiatt 1981), that some of the problems associated with dining result from residents not being able to see the food clearly. Plain tablecloths or placemats can not only make the table more attractive, but also can increase the visual contrast between table and plates, thereby reducing the number of accidents and spills resulting from visual acuity problems. (See Figure 10-1.)

Residents should be allowed to choose their favorite placemat color. A dark floor, white tables with white legs, bright contrasting placemats, and alternating light and dark food on the plates also make it easier for residents to see their food and understand what is expected of them.

Slightly oversized plates and bowls are often easier for residents to manage than smaller plates which have food crowded on them. Royal Doulton now makes a china that is especially well suited for the ARD population (Koncelik 1976). The plates have a raised edge, and the cups have two handles, making them easier to hold. Silverware with slightly oversized handles is easier to grip, but must be well weighted and balanced. Feather-light utensils are harder to use.

*Figure 10-2 Dining Room. Source: Heather Hill, Chardon, OH.*

*Figure 10-2 Dining Room. Source: Heather Hill, Chardon, OH.*

Styrofoam cups tip easily, and should be avoided. An occupational therapist will be able to provide a number of adapted utensils to promote self-feeding and independence.

**Group Size.** Most people are used to eating in relatively small groups (2-6 people) (Hiatt 1981; Hiatt 1983). Seating four or six at a table not only makes the group more manageable in terms of stimulation, but also is easier on residents' neck and back muscles than trying to socialize while seated side-by-side. One or two tables seating only two people should also be available. Tables with straight sides (four, six, or eight) will be easier for residents to set because each "territory" is more clearly defined. There should always be enough space between tables to allow easy passage through the space for wheelchair-bound residents. (See Figure 10-2.)

Facilities should also consider alternatives to the "central dining room" theme. If hallways are designed with nooks, residents might prefer to eat in these relatively more intimate settings, seeing them as more reminiscent of home. Even if there is only one such area, it can provide a semiprivate dining area when friends and family visit. If establishment of separate dining areas on the unit is not feasible, the dining room should, if possible, be partitioned into smaller areas. Many restaurants now do this with, for instance, fabric panels hung from the ceiling to visually divide the large space into smaller, more manageable units. Low walls with a trellis or plants can serve the same purpose. Changes in ceiling height can also be used, but this type of change might not be as obvious to some residents.

E

**Noise.** One of the greatest problems associated with meals in institutions is noise. Noise from ventilation systems, motorized ice machines, kitchen work, metal carts, and even unnecessary background music can add to the din and general confusion. Hard walls only reflect existing sounds; acoustic ceiling tiles and fire-resistant quilts or wall hangings can reduce noise levels. As in hallways, wall carpet on the lower half of the wall can work well in dining areas. If noise is not a problem, soft background music can be pleasant.

**Smells.** Cooking smells can be an effective way to stimulate hunger, indicate that it is mealtime, remind residents of prior eating patterns, and indicate what is to come (Hiatt 1981). Yeast, lemon butter, garlic, tomato, and fresh coffee can be useful in this regard. The introduction of cooking smells can be especially effective with ethnic or other populations that have traditionally had special food-related rituals.

*Social Supports*

It is important to determine the eating habits each resident held prior to the onset of dementing disease. Concerted efforts to follow these patterns will decrease agitation, lead to fewer catastrophic reactions, and, possibly, improve nutritional intake. Staff should arrange to talk with families just prior to admission to ascertain new residents' preferences. This will make the move to the unit much more pleasant and less catastrophic.

Some people prefer eating alone, always. Others might prefer eating breakfast alone, but having other meals in the company of others. Some people eat without talking, while others consider meals a time to socialize. Knowing these individual habits, and encouraging residents to continue them, is beneficial.

A pleasant, quiet, therapeutically supportive environment can go a long way toward increasing a resident's competence in dining. However, some residents might still need reminders from staff on appropriate behaviors, use of utensils, etc. Dining can also be used as a therapeutic activity, stimulating the mind and the body. Special activities before and after meals can heighten the therapeutic advantages. For instance, a special meal can be used as a basis for reminiscence and sharing between residents.

## Way-finding/Orientation

*Definition:*

The process by which the environment helps a person derive cues and information to aid in navigation from a point through space to a desired location.

*Behavioral Considerations*

The fact that there are three meals served every day adds consistency to the life of the confused individual. However, the cognitively impaired person is less able to remember the location of the dining room and might have to "discover it" every time. The ability to know when and how to get to the dining room increases feelings of competence.

*Design Response*

A dining room which looks like a dining room, as opposed to a multipurpose area, increases residents' capacity to recognize it. A room that looks like it serves a typical "family-sized" group will be even more readily recognized. The use of small tables seating four or six persons will also help cue residents about the use of the room. (See Figure 10-3.)

Especially if the dining room is part of a larger shared living space, it should be visually and acoustically distinctive. The Weiss Institute at the Philadelphia Geriatric Center uses a half-wall, columns, and a change in floor color to visually distinguish the dining area from the rest of the unit (see Figure 10-4).

*Figure 10-3* Dining
Room. *Source: Wesley
Hall, Chelsea
Methodist Home,
Chelsea, MI, and
Institute of
Gerontology,
University of
Michigan, Ann Arbor,
MI.*

*Figure 10-4* View to
the Dining Room.
*Source: Philadelphia
Geriatric Center,
Philadelphia, PA.
Photograph by Harry
Finberg.*

If the dining room is also used as an activities room, it is beneficial to somehow change the character of the room at mealtime in order to cue appropriate behavior. Bright placemats or tablecloths on the tables are excellent, easy cues to this change in use. Graphics should not add to the residents' confusion. Residents who follow signs to the dining room but end up in the multipurpose room are likely to be more confused and agitated. A multiple-use room should have a name—the fellowship room, the atrium, the green room— whatever seems appropriate.

Appropriate cues should also be used if smaller seating nooks/areas on the unit (as opposed to one central room) are to be used for dining. Tables which fold up from the walls can be easily "stored" out of the way during nonmeal times, but unfolded and set to indicate that it is mealtime. Appropriate dining chairs with arms should be available; comfortable lounge and armchairs are not appropriate for meals.

Another solution that has been tried, with varying success, is tables hung from the ceiling. The advantages are that there are no table legs to interfere with wheelchairs, they store easily and do not require an extra storage room. One disadvantage is that this arrangement is not at all residential in character. Other disadvantages include awkward trusses from the center of the table that are hard for residents to see around, and added confusion and disorientation for the residents when tables are pulled down from the ceiling. Only if space is *extremely limited* might this strategy be appropriate. If hanging tables is the only alternative, the table bottoms can be painted either to blend with the ceiling and be less noticeable, or to create an interesting, unique pattern (see Figure 10-5).

**Figure 10-5** Ceiling
Hung Tables. Source:
Northview Home for
Mental Health,
Waukesha, WI.

DINING ROOM

*Figure 10-6 Dining
Room Signage.*

**Signage.** If the dining room is not immediately visible from the other major public areas of the unit, additional environmental cues to its location will be needed (assuming there is one central dining room). Signs with large clear letters can be used effectively; graphics—for instance, a picture of a place setting—can also help (see Chapter 6 for more detail about sign use and placement.) See Figure 10-6.

*Chapter 11*

# Kitchen

---

## Safety and Security

*Definition:*

The degree to which the environment is designed to avoid the occurrence or accidents while not inhibiting the ease of locomotion through, and use of, the environment.

*Behavioral Considerations*

People with dementia are not as aware as unimpaired individuals of the consequences of their actions. Kitchens are full of potentially hazardous appliances and objects, so they must be designed with extra caution.

A highly visible kitchenette encourages more residential use.

*Design Response*

Most institutions find that it is not feasible to have all food prepared on the unit. But occasional meals, special treats, and easy access to food for snacks can be beneficial, and make the staff routine easier. The more "residential" the kitchenette and appliances, the easier it is for residents to complete tasks on their own. (See Figure 11-1.)

*Figure 11-1 Kitchen. Source: Wesley Hall, Chelsea Methodist Home, Chelsea, MI, and Institute of Gerontology, University of Michigan, Ann Arbor, MI.*

H

H

**Workspace.** Fewer accidents are likely to occur in the kitchen if each resident in the room has his or her own work space. A table located conveniently near the counters will allow residents to sit while working and decrease the number of distractions from other objects, appliances, or switches within easy reach.

**Lock systems.** If constant staff observation of the kitchenette is not feasible, at least one of several safety precautions must be taken. One solution would be to lock the kitchenette so that residents have access to it only when staff members are present. Another is to have the kitchenette basically accessible, but to close it off selectively when access needs to be strictly limited. (See Figure 11-2.)

While locking the kitchen might seem to be the safest course, it does not allow residents easy access to nonhazardous kitchenette areas, for instance to get a cup of coffee or a drink. It decreases their level of control.

Therefore another solution which should be considered would be to restrict access only to those appliances or objects that are potentially hazardous and easily misused. The stove should be equipped with a timer or separate power switch to which only staff have access (see Figures 11-1 and 11-3).

*Figure 11-2*
*Kitchenette.*
*Source: Cedar Lakes*
*Home Campus, West*
*Bend, WI.*

This will ensure that staff are aware when someone is using the stove so they can increase supervision, but allows residents access to other areas of the kitchenette. Another useful option is a refrigerator with the cooling control knob inaccessible to residents. This can prevent a lot of spoiled food. In addition, some drawers or cabinets should be equipped with locks to protect residents who use utensils improperly. Cleaning agents should also be kept in a locked cabinet. The locks should be inconspicuous (see Figure 5-4).

H

**Storage.** Dangerous equipment (food processor, electric can opener, disposal, blender) should not be accessible to residents. The designer might also remember that many of these timesaving devices take away from potentially therapeutic residential activities, like chopping food.

*Social Supports*

All prolonged or complicated kitchen activities should be supervised by staff because of the potential hazards. But residents should be encouraged to do as many of the individual activities/tasks as possible.

*Figure 11-3 Timer for Appliances.*

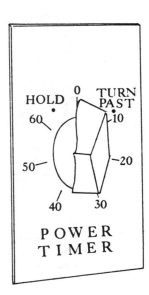

## Activities of Daily Living

*Definition:*     The extent to which the environment facilitates or inhibits the residents' abilities to carry out daily living activities.

*Behavioral Considerations*     Food preparation is not only necessary for life, it can also be a source of pride and joy. This is especially true for the older female population. These residents will quite likely find it disturbing, frustrating, and confusing to have no access to a kitchen, even if they do not prepare all their meals. And while not capable of preparing complete meals, they can still do many of the single tasks necessary to that procedure. Because many of these tasks require concentration, they are excellent therapeutically. The opportunity to continue working in this realm can give (particularly female) residents feelings of competence and increased self-respect.

Most residents had free access to a kitchen before moving to the unit, and have preferred snacks and snack times. Access to a kitchenette lets people continue to exert some control over this part of their lives.

*Design Response*

If residents are to be encouraged to participate in activities in the kitchenette that area should be as residential as possible. This will increase residents' ability to understand where utensils, dishes, and cookware are kept. Many of the following suggestions are slight prosthetic adjustments to a standard residential kitchen (see Figure 11-1).

E

**Counters.** Counters should be 2-3 inches below standard height, because older people, especially older women, tend to be shorter and to stoop more than the general population (for whom standard counter heights were set). All corners should be rounded. It might also be helpful to have a kitchen table available to give residents a place to sit and rest and to increase the amount of workspace available.

E

**Cabinets.** As many cabinets as possible should be placed below the counter and/or wall-hung. Reaching into above-counter cabinets is more difficult and dangerous for residents; visibility is reduced, and residents are more likely to drop a stack of plates if they have to pull them down from overhead. All cabinets (except for limited access cabinets—see safety section) should have large handles which do not have sharp edges. If residents are allowed to keep their own food in the kitchenette, clear labels on shelves or cabinets might avoid unconscious "borrowing" by some residents. Labels also help residents find the proper location of dishes and cookware when they are preparing a meal or cleaning up afterwards (see Figure 11-1).

**Appliances.** As mentioned in the safety section, appliances, including can openers, blenders, ranges, and coffeemakers, that might commonly be found in a home will be easier for the residents to use. Care should be taken not leave too many small appliances out on the counter for residents to have to choose among (also see safety). Other appliances can actually be the center of therapies. An ice cream maker, for instance, can be fun to use, and the whole unit will be able to partake of the results.

E

**Sink.** Hand-washing dishes is enjoyable for some residents. A double sink is better for this purpose than a single sink. An aluminum basin is easier to clean and more forgiving than porcelain, and will lead to fewer broken dishes. The kitchen sink should be low enough (approximately 33–34 inches from the floor) to allow easy elbow clearance. A lower sink, without a front or with doors that can be opened but which has no shelves or kickboard, makes for easier wheelchair access. Retractable water faucets are not advisable, since residents are likely to try to clean counters, windows, floors, etc. with them. Whenever possible, the sink should be located by a window. If this is not possible, the view while standing at the sink should be pleasant.

E

**Walls.** It is advisable to tile the wall above the kitchen counter. Tiles now can be purchased in a variety of colors and patterns. Scrubbable wallpaper above the tile can add a nice, homelike touch, and is easier to clean than a painted surface. Wallpaper can be helpful as well as convenient, especially if the rest of the unit is painted, since it helps to distinguish the kitchenette as a separate area.

E

**Floor.** The kitchen floor should be easily cleanable, but not slippery when wet. Padded vinyl is good, and comes in 12-foot rolls, so there are few seams. If a solid color is used, dropped food or utensils are easily visible. An inconspicuous floor drain should be included if possible.

E/H

**Lighting.** Lighting in a kitchen area should be more intense than that in other areas. Lights hung on the underside of above-counter cabinets will decrease the shadows caused by overhead ceiling fixtures.

*Social Supports*

Food preparation requires many complicated tasks, but many residents will still be able to engage in these various activities if staff members direct them and divide complex chores into single, simpler tasks. Some residents will also need to be reminded of how to use certain appliances and gadgets—a can opener, for instance. It should be remembered that people who did not spend time in a kitchen before entering the unit will probably not want to do so once they have arrived (although there will be exceptions).

*Chapter 12*

# Outdoor Spaces

---

## Privacy and Socialization

*Definition:*

The degree to which the environment inhibits or facilitates opportunities for a person to control amounts of privacy and social contact between people.

*Behavioral Considerations*

Access to outdoor spaces for fresh air and sensory stimulation is important for everyone, but is especially important for residents of a limited access unit. It enriches their experiences and allows greater variety in their immediate physical surroundings. Spaces that vary in size, location, and amount of sun allow residents to feel they have control over their interactions with other people and with the outdoors.

## E/H

*Design Response*

Direct access to an enclosed courtyard is almost always considered a high priority design element. Because people with dementia are often very active, an enclosed, restrictive environment (i.e., a limited access unit) can be a source of frustration and tension. A courtyard that is directly accessible from the unit greatly increases residents' options in seeking out privacy and social interaction. Ideally, the staff should have easy visual access to the courtyard and be

109

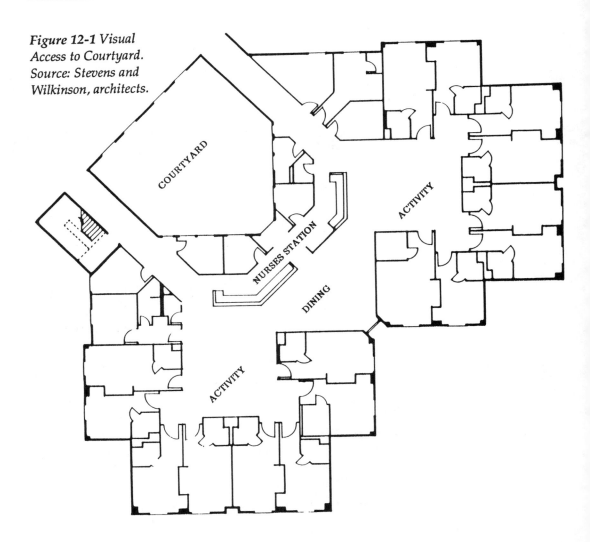

*Figure 12-1 Visual Access to Courtyard. Source: Stevens and Wilkinson, architects.*

able to monitor residents' activities at all times. This will increase significantly the chances that the yard will be used frequently by the residents. (See Figure 12-1.)

A well designed courtyard provides opportunities for both active and passive pleasures: gardening, socializing with friends or relatives, sitting in the sun, exploration, and group activities. There should be numerous seating nooks accommodating single persons, small groups (2-4), and larger groups (6-10). Shade should also be provided, as

*Figure 12-2*
*Courtyard. Source:*
*Heather Hill, Chardon,*
*OH.*

E

E

direct sunlight can be too bright for many elderly. Umbrella tables are often a good solution, as is extending part of the roof over a patio, which allows residents to sit outside during a gentle rain. (See Figure 12-2.)

Raised planters along paths or by benches make it easier for residents to participate in gardening activities. The use of separate, moderate-sized planters (12 x 24 inches) allows residents who enjoy gardening to have their own space to pursue that activity individually when so desired. A community plot, possibly planted with herbs or vegetables, can encourage residents to work together. Raised planters also help bring flowers and plants to a more accessible level for residents confined to wheelchairs. Care should be taken to use only nonpoisonous plants, because some residents may try to eat them.

A swing or gazebo can be a focal point that not only adds visual interest, but draws residents together. Other ideas include landscaping with interesting historical artifacts, which can encourage residents to reflect on past experiences. A series of therapeutic parks designed by Rapelji, Papp, and Crawford (1981) included a 200-year-old horse-drawn buggy, a 100-year-old plow and cultivator, and an old water pump.

## Safety and Security

*Definition:* The degree to which the environment is designed to avoid the occurrence of accidents while not inhibiting the ease of locomotion through, and use of, the environment.

*Behavioral Considerations*

Some residents might try to "go home" or wander elsewhere; therefore, a limited access courtyard is important unless there is to be constant supervision when residents are outside. If enclosing walls are present, residents might try to climb them. This might occur less frequently if walls or fences are neither obvious nor easily accessible.

The older person's kinesthetic abilities decrease. Therefore, it is important that the surfaces of paths be level; cracks or changes in level are likely to cause accidents.

**E**

*Design Response*

**Walls.** The existence of walls or fences not only prevents wandering off the grounds, but makes some residents more comfortable because it decreases their fear that they will become lost. The problem is to enclose the courtyard without repeating the often familiar theme of restraint and confinement. Planted vines can create a more pleasant wall; bushes in front decrease accessibility to it. Other alternatives are ornate, split log, or white picket fencing, as long as residents cannot climb them easily.

**E/H**

**Paths.** All paths should have even surfaces, but the textures can vary. For example, interlocking bricks can be used at one point, and colored cement at another. This use of texture can enhance way-finding abilities. Paths should also be well lit for twilight strolls.

**E/H**

**Furniture.** Brightly colored furniture adds visual interest to a park or courtyard as it increases the area's visibility. Furniture should be placed on flat, solid surfaces. There should also be lights for evening activities. Rapelji, Papp and Crawford (1981) used old-fashioned streetlamps to add character in addition to light.

# Chapter 13

# Nursing Station/ Staff Areas

## Nursing Station

*Behavioral Considerations*

Staff on the unit need to have clear visual access to the residents at all times.

*Design Response*

There are two distinct philosophies concerning the appropriate design of a nursing station for a special care unit. The first follows the traditional nursing home and medical model: a reasonably large, clearly visible station. Such a station usually has clear visual access to most (if not all) of shared living spaces and the corridor. This allows staff members to monitor all ongoing activities as they are charting and completing other duties. The front of the station, however, must not be so high that staff cannot see wheelchair-bound residents over the top of the counter. (See Figure 13-1.)

The other philosophy holds that increasing the interpersonal contact between staff and residents, which is of primary concern with the cognitively impaired population, is best accomplished by reducing the size and scale of the station drastically, until it is little more than a desk. The desk can be placed directly in the shared living area, or in an adjacent room. (See Figures 13-2 and 13-3.)

Charting can be done at this desk, or staff can be given time off the unit to do the charting. With this arrangement,

113

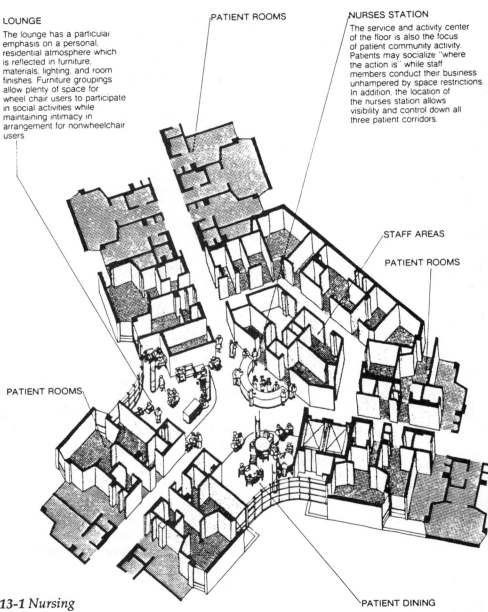

**LOUNGE**

The lounge has a particular emphasis on a personal, residential atmosphere which is reflected in furniture, materials, lighting, and room finishes. Furniture groupings allow plenty of space for wheel chair users to participate in social activities while maintaining intimacy in arrangement for nonwheelchair users.

PATIENT ROOMS

**NURSES STATION**

The service and activity center of the floor is also the focus of patient community activity. Patients may socialize "where the action is" while staff members conduct their business unhampered by space restrictions. In addition, the location of the nurses station allows visibility and control down all three patient corridors.

STAFF AREAS

PATIENT ROOMS

PATIENT ROOMS

*Figure 13-1 Nursing Station as a Landmark. Source: Florence Hamd Home, Lagrange, GA, Stevens and Wilkinson, architects.*

**axonometric view
patient common areas**

**PATIENT DINING**

Patients are encouraged to leave their rooms for all meals. Those patients who cannot use the main cafeteria will be served in their floor dining commons. This area also functions as a game and party space.

*Figure 13-2 Nursing Station in the Day Room. Source: Cedar Lakes Home Campus, West Bend, WI.*

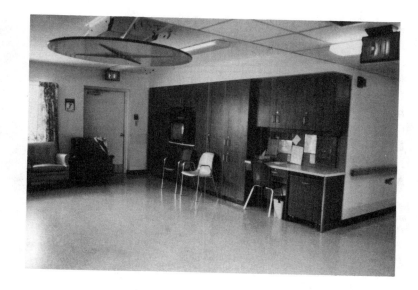

staff cannot "hide" behind the station, but are out on the unit with the residents.

There is no evidence to suggest that one approach to nursing station design is necessarily better than the other. The success of any station plan relates to many factors: size of the unit, degree of competence of the residents, staff training, and the organization and physical structure of the unit. More research needs to be done to weigh all the pros and cons of both solutions to see which works best, and under what conditions.

## Respite Areas

*Behavioral Considerations*

Working with an ARD population on a daily basis is a demanding job. Staff members need a place off the unit to relax and regroup. Some staff find it difficult to chart while on the unit, and can be more efficient when this is done in a separate area.

*Design Response*

Regardless of the design of the nursing station, a staff respite room or area is essential. It should have both comfortable chairs and/or sofas and tables to work at. The size will vary depending on the number of staff, frequency

*Figure 13-3 Nursing Desk. Source: Wesley Hall, Chelsea Methodist Home, Chelsea, MI, and Institute of Gerontology, University of Michigan, Ann Arbor, MI.*

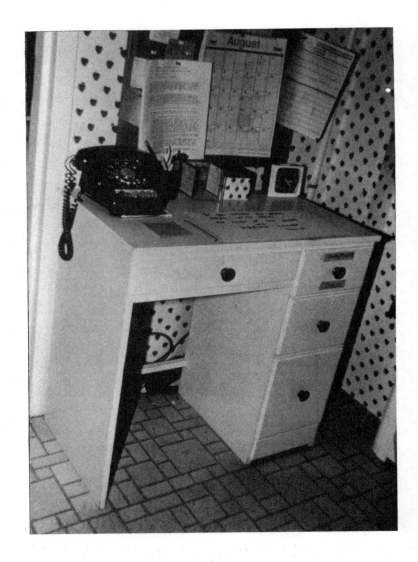

of use and type of use (charting, staff meetings, staff dining, etc.) The provision of a kitchenette increases the likelyhood that staff will use the room.

If this staff respite area is not immediately adjacent to the unit it should be equipped with a 2-way intercom so that staff on the unit can summon extra assistance in an emergency.

*Chapter 14*

# Design Review
# Checklist

## Introduction

This chapter is intended to be used either as a review of plans for a special care unit or as an evaluative tool in existing units. If the unit is already constructed, it is suggested that this review be completed during a walk-through tour.

Each section begins with a short description of the environment-behavioral issues most important to the goal of maximizing functional independence. The questions then highlight particular areas of concern (signage, socialization, safety, etc.).

## Basic Design Issues

Special consideration must be given to the environment of people with dementia due to the cognitive impairments associated with their illness. Most such persons are aged 65 or older, and experience the typical age-related decreases in sensory perceptions in addition to their disease symptoms. The environment must compensate also for these disabilities.

- Is the layout of the unit easy to understand? Too many corners and hidden areas will exacerbate the disabilities for this population.

- Is resident access to unsafe areas restricted? Are methods of controlling access designed to decrease agitation about this limited access?

- Is the lighting sufficient for the elderly eye, without unnecessary glare? Do surfaces, walls, and/or floors reflect light? Has direct sunlight from windows been diffused?

- Is there enough visual contrast between objects and backgrounds? Between the floor and the wall?

- Are railings in the corridors designed to be easily used by both frail ambulatory residents and those confined to wheelchairs?

- Is furniture sturdy enough for residents to lean on for support? Is it in good repair? Does it look residential?

- If there is carpeting, is it clean? Is there an odor? Is it a tight weave to decrease the problems of mobility for wheelchair-bound residents?

- Are there covers over all unused wall sockets?

- Are plants nonpoisonous?

## Bedrooms

The bedroom is where residents are most able to express their individual identities. It is essential to support this personalization process if a resident is to make the unit "home." The bedroom is also the scene of many of the most obvious failures in competencies related to self-maintainence (dressing, grooming, etc.), and should be designed to enhance remaining abilities. Because residents spend time in their rooms without supervision, close attention to safety is also important. Finally, the ability to find one's room independently is an important factor in maintaining individual residents' dignity.

- Does each room reflect the resident's identity (personal furniture, bedspread, wall hangings, display area)?

- Are rooms visually distinctive, or are all rooms given the same wall color and curtain treatment?

- Can residents manipulate the window(s) and curtains?

- Are there mirrors for use in grooming?

- Does the closet door open to allow clear visual access to the inside?

- Is there enough enclosed storage space that residents' closets do not present an overwhelming array of choices?

- Are there aids to assist in dressing (signs on the drawers, a special closet)?

- Is the window opening small enough to keep residents from climbing out?

- If there are any throw rugs, are they secure on the floor, or do they slip?

- If there are any locks, are they inconspicuous and used only when necessary?

- Does there appear to be sufficient storage space for nonseasonal items?

- Is each bedroom visually distinct (use of color, personalized signs or mementos)?

- Are signs visible to residents walking down the hall (consider height, size of lettering, location on hall or inside door)?

- Is there a change in floor color between the hall and the room?

## Corridors

Prosthetic environmental supports to aid in way-finding are often necessary for the ARD population. The primary goal is to increase the amount of information that residents can understand, either through personalized cues or increased visual distinctiveness of different areas and rooms. The provision of nooks to increase opportunities for casual social interaction, or of areas to watch others privately, is also suggested.

- If there are several halls, are they visually distinct (color, wall treatment, thematic artwork)?

- Are signs clearly visible (height, location at decision points, clear lettering, understandable, eye-catching graphics)?

- Are there other latent cues available to help orient residents (i.e., use of plants or furniture to indicate a specific room's location)?

- Are there areas set off from the corridor that provide opportunities for casual interaction?

- Do these areas or nooks have views of pleasant or interesting scenes (outside, the living room, the nursing station)?

- Are there "interactive" or tactile wall hangings for the residents to explore?

- Is glare a problem (highly polished or reflective surfaces, bright spots of light)?

- Are corridors more than 50 feet long without a change of direction?

# Hygiene Facilities

Toileting and personal care are typically thought of as private activities. This should not necessarily change upon moving to a special care unit. Encouraging and supporting independence in this area increase a resident's feelings of competence and self-respect. A major component of this self-sufficiency lies in being able to locate the toilet rooms without having to ask for assistance. When assistance is necessary, the environment should not hinder staff activities.

- Are there private or semiprivate toilets for each bedroom?

- Are toilets clearly visible from inside the room?

- If there are shared hygiene facilities, are they visually distinct from the hallway? (color, signage, individualized entries, i.e., canopy)?

- If there are shared hygiene facilities, are they adjacent to the main shared living areas?

- Is the men's room distinct from the women's?

- Is the color and pattern from outside carried inside the room?

- Is the floor tile, terrazzo, or another hard surface or is it padded and more forgiving in case of a fall?

- Are the mirrors positioned so that seated residents can see themselves from the waist up?

- Is the lighting flattering to the person standing at the mirrors?

- Is there personal storage space for each resident?

- Is there access to both a shower and a tub, with grab bars, tub seats, and other prosthetic devices?

- Is there enough room for staff to assist residents during bathing?

- Is there accessible storage space for bathing supplies?

- Is there a floor drain in each bathing area?

- Is there good ventilation in all tub/shower areas?

## Shared Living Areas

Shared living areas that are reminiscent of home settings not only make residents feel more at ease, they can remind residents of appropriate behaviors. A "homelike" atmosphere should be reflected in the size of the rooms and the style and arrangement of furniture. Increasing the personalization of common areas by hanging artwork by the residents; framed, enlarged photographs of residents, or thematic posters about recent events also can help residents feel more at home.

- Are the shared living areas designed to support small group activities (4–6 people)?

- Is furniture residential in appearance?

- Are chairs placed at right angles to each other to encourage social interaction?

- Are there opportunities for residents to engage in activities at will (card tables with cards, puzzles, books and magazines, laundry to fold)?

- Is there any furniture brought in by the residents (favorite chairs, chests, etc.)?

- Is noise a problem?

- Are there opportunities for one or two people to observe ongoing activities?

- If there are wanderers, are there living rooms at different ends of the most-used wandering path(s)?

- Do items hung on the walls reflect the lives of the residents (artwork done by residents, pictures brought from home, enlarged and framed pictures of the residents)?

- Is there any display that encourages residents to look at and talk about (resident of the month, collage of unit activities)?

# Dining room

Dining room design should support the remaining abilities of the residents, not remind them of lost ones. Special attention to flexibility, in order to meet the needs and wishes of the greatest number of residents, can increase feelings of self-sufficiency and dignity. An overstimulating environment, however, can increase agitation and confusion.

- Does the dining room provide opportunities for residents to eat in small groups (2–6)?

- If the dining room is large, is it subdivided to make it appear smaller (half-walls, hanging curtains, partitions, plants)?

- Do tables have straight sides to make it easier for residents to set the tables (if appropriate)?

- Is there enough room to accommodate wheelchairs?

- Is the dining room easy to find from the central living area (either adjacent and visible, or through appropriate signage)?

- Is there an area or room somewhat removed from the main dining room where families can share meals with their relatives?

- Is there a noise problem?

## Kitchen

A kitchenette can provide many opportunities for residents to participate in group activities and then take pride in accomplished tasks. For many residents, this represents a continuation of patterns established over a lifetime. But there are also increased opportunities for accidents to occur, so safety issues are of concern.

- Does the kitchenette look "residential"?

- Is there space available in the kitchen or nearby for individual work surfaces?

- Is the lighting brighter than in other areas of the unit?

- Are counters 32–34 inches high (below standard height)?

- Are unnecessary appliances (electric can openers, food processors) kept to a minimum?

- Does the stove have limited access (timer or lock device)?

- Are there locks on some of the drawers or cabinets to allow safe storage of potentially harmful cleaning agents and utensils?

# Outdoor Spaces

Direct access to a courtyard is often considered to be one of the highest priorities in creating a special care unit because it affords increased opportunities for fresh air, a change of scenery, and most importantly, exercise. It should allow a variety of solitary and group activities and include a variety of stimulating experiences.

- Is there direct access to an enclosed or limited-access courtyard?

- Do staff have direct visual access to the courtyard from the unit or nursing station?

- Does the courtyard provide opportunities for small and large group activities?

- Are there chairs or benches where people can sit and enjoy the fresh air?

- Are there both sunny and shady areas?

- Are there objects of visual interest in the courtyard (a gazebo, an old-fashioned pump, etc.)

- Are residents encouraged to participate in gardening activities?

- Are paths well maintained, with no ruts or holes?

# Entry to the Unit

While not discussed as a separate area in the design guide, the entry to the unit is important because it is often part of a visitor's first impression of the unit. Attention to the design of this area can decrease residents' desire to "escape," and lessen the common problem of congregation of residents around the locked door to the unit.

- Are there residents standing or sitting around the entry, as if waiting for someone to enter?

- Are residents able to see directly into areas they do not have access to? (This increases their desire to get off the unit.)

- Does the door to the unit call attention to itself from inside the unit, with artwork or different treatment, thus increasing its interest to the residents?

- Is there a clear line of sight to either a nursing station or shared living space?

- Is the entry attractive from outside the unit, and does it give a pleasant first impression?

# References and Bibliography

Aldrich, C.K. and E. Mendkoff. 1963. Relocation of the aged and disabled: A mortality study. *Journal of the American Geriatrics Society* 11:185–194.

Allport, G.W. 1961. *Pattern and growth in personality*. New York: Holt, Rinehart and Winston.

Altman, I. 1975. *Environment and social behavior: Privacy, personal space, territoriality and crowding*. Monterey, CA: Brooks-Cole.

Altman, I., M.P. Lawton, and J.F. Wohlwill, eds. 1984. Elderly people and the environment. *Human behavior and the environment* vol 7. New York: Plenum Publishing Co., Inc.

Alvermann, M. 1979. Towards improving geriatric care with environmental interventions emphasizing a homelike atmosphere: An environmental experience. *Journal of Gerontological Nursing* 5(3):13–17.

Alzheimer's Disease and Related Disorders Association. 1984. What is Alzheimer's disease? We care nursing pamphlet. Milwaukee, WI: ADRDA

Alzheimer's disease: A devastating illness. 1984. *Aging in the News* 75:14

Andreason, M.E. 1985. Make an environment safe by design. *Journal of Gerontological Nursing* 11(6): 19–22.

Antoine, M., C. Holland, and B. Scruggs. 1986. Measuring improvement in patients with dementia. *Geriatric Nursing* 7(4):185–189.

Archea, J. 1982. Conceptual and methodological conflicts in applied interdisciplinary research on environ-ment and aging. In *Aging and environment: Theoretical approaches*. Eds. M.P. Lawton, P. Windley, and T. Byerts. New York: Springer Publishing Co.

Archea, J. and S. Margulis. 1979. Environmental research inputs to policy and design programs: The case of preparation for the involuntary relocation of institutionalized aged. In *Environmental context of aging: Life styles and environmental quality and living arrangements*. Eds. T. Byerts, S. Howell, and L. Pastalan. New York: Garland STPM Press.

Arneill, B.P. 1984. Private hilltop village offers residents every amenity of home. *Hospitals* 2:90–92

Atlanta Chapter, Alzheimer's Disease and Related Disorders Association. 1985. *Understanding and caring for the person with Alzheimer's disease: A practical guide*. Atlanta: ADRDA

Averill, J.R. 1973. Personal control over aversive stimuli and its relationship to stress. *Psychological Bulletin* 80:286–303.

Banziger, G. and S. Roush. 1983. Nursing homes for the birds: A control-relevant intervention with bird feeders. *The Gerontologist* 23:527–531.

Barnes, R.D. 1981. Perceived freedom and control in the built environment. In *Cognition, social behavior and the environment*. Ed. J. Harvey. Hillsdale, NY: Lawrence Erlbaum Associates.

Barnes, P.D., M.A. Raskind, and M. Scott. 1981. Problems of families caring for Alzheimer's patients: Use of a support group. *Journal of the American Geriatric Society* 29(80):80–85.

Barton, M. and D. Mishkin. 1984a. Behavior patterns related to spatially differentiated areas of a psychiatric ward dayroom. In *Institutional setting: An environmental design approach*. Ed. M. Spivack. New York: Human Sciences Press.

Barton, M. and D. Mishkin. 1984b. Ratings of experimental play and learning settings for emotionally disturbed and mentally retarded children. In *Institutional settings: An environmental design approach*. Ed. M. Spivack. New York: Human Sciences Press.

Barton, M. and P. Powell, 1984. The effect of angle of light in the recognition and evaluation of faces. In *Institutional settings: An environmental design approach*. Ed. M. Spivack. New York: Human Sciences Press.

Baum, A. and J. Singer, eds. 1980. *Advances in environmental psychology Vol. 2: Application of personal control*. Hillsdale, NJ: Lawrence Erlbaum Associates.

Beam, I.M. 1984. Helping families survive. *American Journal of Nursing* 84(2):229–232.

Beck, P. 1982. Two successful interventions in nursing homes: The therapeutic effects of cognitive activity. *The Gerontologist* 22(4):378–383.

Beck, W. and T. Meyer, eds. 1984. *Institutional care environments: The users viewpoint*. Boca Raton, FL: CRC Press.

Becker, F.D. 1980. Employees need a role in design of work space. *Hospitals* 54:97–101.

Bednar, M.J. 1977. *Barrier free environments*. Stroudsburg PA: Dowden Hutchinson and Ross, Inc.

Bell, T. 1967. The relationship between social involvement and feeling old among residents in homes for the aged. *Journal of Gerontology* 22:17–22.

Berg, S. et al. 1977. Milieu treatment in a ward for psychiatric long term care. *Scandinavian Journal of Social Medicine* Supplement 14:163–172.

Berkman, L.F. 1983. The assessment of social networks and social support in the elderly. *Journal of the American Geriatrics Society* 31(12):742–749.

Bourestom, N. and L. Pastalan. 1983. Final report: Forced relocation: Setting, staff and patient effects. Grant 5RO MH20747-02. Ann Arbor, University of Michigan.

Bourestom, N. and L. Pastalan. 1981. The effects of relocation on the elderly: A reply to Borup, Gallego and Hefferman. *The Gerontologist* 2(1):4–7.

Bowersox, J. 1984. Design recommendations for housing and long term care facilities for the elderly. Testimony before the U.S. House of Representative Select Committee on Aging. May 22, 1984.

Burnside, I.M. 1981. Psychological issues in nursing care of the aged. *Journal of Gerontological Nursing.* 7(11):689–694.

Burnside, I.M. 1980. You have been here before. *Journal of Gerontological Nursing* 6(7):3.

Calkins, M.P. 1987. Designing special care units: A systematic approach. *The American Journal of Alzheimer's Care and Research* 2(3):30–34.

Calkins, M.P. 1987. Designing special care units: A systematic approach. *The American Journal of Alzheimer's Care and Research* 2(2):30–34.

Carp, F.M. 1977. Impact of improved living environment on health and life expectancy. *The Gerontologist* 17:242–249.

Carp, F.M. 1976. A senior center in public housing for the elderly. *The Gerontologist* 16:243–249.

Carpman, J.R., M. Grant, and D. Simmons. 1985. *No more mazes: Research abut design and wayfinding in hospitals.* Ann Arbor, MI: University of Michigan Press.

Cavens, A. 1981. Leave me alone: I have to stay in bed. *Washington Nurse* 11:6.

Clark, M. et al. 1984. A slow death of the mind. *Newsweek.* December 3:56–62.

Clark, R. 1984. Market needs mold nursing home mission for an older hospital. *Hospitals* 10:96–97.

Cohen, D. and C. Eisdorfer. 1986. The costs of caring. *The American Journal of Alzheimer's Care and Research* 1(3):26–33.

Cohen, D., G. Kennedy, and C. Eisdorfer. 1984. Phases of change in the patient with Alzheimer's disease: A conceptual dimension for defining health care management. *Journal of the American Geriatrics Society* 32(1):11–15.

Coons, D. 1986. Considerations in designing therapeutic environments for people with dementia. Ann Arbor, MI: Institute of Gerontology, University of Michigan. unpublished.

Coons D. 1985. Alive and well at Wesley Hall. *Quarterly, A Journal of Long Term Care* 121(2):10–14.

Corker, E. 1982. Strained relations. *Nursing Mirror* 55(4):32–34.

Cox, K. 1985. Milieu therapy. *Geriatric Nursing* 6(3):152–156.

Cremer, R. and E.J. Zeef. 1987. What kind of noise increases with age? *Journal of Gerontology* 42(5):515–518.

Davidoff, D.A. 1986. Issues in the clinical diagnosis of Alzheimer's disease. *The American Journal of Alzheimer's Care and Research* 1(1):9–15.

Davidson, R. 1978. The problem of senile dementia. *Nursing Times* 6:932–933.

Designing facilities for the elderly. 1978. *The Construction Specifier* 4:6–17.

Devlin, A.S. 1980. Housing for the elderly: Cognitive consideration. *Environment and behavior* 12:451–455.

Eisdorfer, C. 1986. The growing toll of Alzheimer's disease. *Provider* 12:4–5.

Eisdorfer, C. 1984. Therapeutic option in long term caring. Paper read at Hillhaven Foundation National Conference on Alzheimer's disease: A challenge for care. Boston, MA: October 5, 1984.

Ernst, P., B. Beran, and F. Safford. 1978. Isolation and the symptoms of chronic brain syndrome. *The Gerontologist* 18:468–470.

Esser, A.H., ed. 1979. *Behavior and environment: The use of space by animals and man.* New York: Plenum Publishing Co., Inc.

Farkos, S.W. 1980. Impact of chronic illness on the patient's spouse. *Health and Social Work* 5(4):39–46.

Fox, P.J. 1986. Alzheimer's disease: A historical overview. *The American Journal of Alzheimer's Care and Research* 1(4):18–24.

Freedman, J.L. 1975. *Crowding and behavior.* New York: Viking Press.

Friedman, F.B. 1981. It isn't senility: The nurse's role in Alzheimer's disease. *Journal of Practical Nursing* 31(2):17–19.

Gaspar, D. 1980. Hollymore hospital dementia service. *Lancet* 1:1402–1405.

Geer, J.H. and E. Maisel. 1972. Evaluating the effects of the prediction-control confound. *Journal of Personality and Social Psychology* 23:314–319.

Gilhooly, M.L. 1984. The impact on care-givers: Factors associated with the psychological well-being of people supporting a demented relative. *British Journal of Medical Psychology* 57:35–44.

Glass, D. and J. Singer. 1972. *Urban stress.* New York: Academic Press.

Glaze, B. 1982. One woman's story. *Journal of Gerontological Nursing* 8(2):67–68.

Good, L.R. and W.E. Hurting. 1978. Evaluation. A mental health facility: It's users and context. *American Institute of Architects Journal* 67:39–41.

Gottlieb, B.H., ed. 1981. *Social networks and social support.* Beverly Hills, CA: Sage Publications.

Gwyther, L. 1985. *Care of Alzheimer's patients: A manual for nursing home staff.* Washington DC: American Health Care Association and Alzheimer's Disease and Related Disorders Association.

Gwyther, L. 1986. Treating behavior as a symptom of illness. *Provider* 13:18–21.

Gwyther, L. and D.G. Blazer. 1984. Family therapy and the dementia patient. *American Family Physician* 29(5):149–156.

Hall, G.R. and K.C. Buckwalter. 1987. Progressively lowered stress threshold: A conceptual model for care of adults with Alzheimer's disease. unpublished.

Hammer, M.L. 1984. Insight, reminiscence, denial, projection: Coping mechanisms of the aged. *Journal Gerontological Nursing* 10(2):45–68, 81.

Haycox, J.A. 1980. Late care of the demented patient: The question of nursing home placement. *New England Journal of Medicine* 303(3):145–165.

Haynie, W. 1982. Independence through security and support. *Nursing Homes* 31:22–26.

Hayter, J. 1982. Helping families of patients with Alzheimer's disease. *Journal of Gerontological Nursing* 8(2):81–86.

Hazelbaker, B. 1982. The living environment: An interior that speaks of home. *American Health Care Association Journal* 11:12–18.

Hemshorn, A. 1985. They call it Alzheimer's disease. *Journal of Gerontological Nursing* 11(1):36–38.

Hershberger, R.G. and C.L. Harris. 1977. Use of gerontological research information in a design studio. *Journal of Architectural Education* 31(1):33–36.

Hiatt, L. 1985. Designing for mentally impaired persons: Integrating knowledge of people with programs, architecture and interior design. Paper read at the American Association of Homes for the Aging annual meeting. Los Angeles, CA.

Hiatt, L. 1984. Conveying the substance of images: Interior design in long term care. *Contemporary Administrator* 6:86–89.

Hiatt, L. 1983. Effective design for informal conversation. *American Health Care Association Journal* 9(2):43–46.

Hiatt, L. 1981. Designing therapeutic dining. *Nursing Homes* 3:33–39.

Hiatt, L. 1980. Disorientation is more than a state of mind. *Nursing Homes* 29(4):30–36.

Hiatt, L. 1979a. Environmental consideration in understanding and designing environments for mentally impaired older people. In *Mentally impaired aging: Bridging the gap.* Washington DC: American Association of Homes for the Aging.

Hiatt, L. 1979b. The importance of the physical environment. *Nursing Homes* 28:2–10.

Hirshfield, M. 1983. Home care versus institutionalization: Family care giving and senile brain disease. *International Journal of Nursing Studies* 20(1):23–32.

Hirst, S. 1983. Alzheimer's disease: A look at the nursing literature. *American Association of Registered Nurses Newsletter* 39(10):3–4.

Holahan, C. 1972. Seating patterns and patient behavior in an experimental dayroom. *Journal of Abnormal Psychology* 80(20):115–124.

Holahan, C. and S. Seagert. 1973. Behavioral and attitudinal effects of large scale variation in the physical environment of psychiatric wards. *Journal of Abnormal Psychology* 82(3):454–462.

Holland, L. et al. 1981. Institutional structure and resident outcomes. *Journal of Health and Social Behavior* 22:433–444.

Howell, A. 1977. The aged as user groups: Aging as a process in design education. *Journal of Architectural Education* 31(1):26–29.

Howell, S. 1980. *Designing for aging: Patterns of use.* Cambridge, MA: MIT Press.

Hull, J. and J. Thompson. 1980. Predicting adaptive functioning of mentally retarded in community settings. *American Journal of Mental Deficiency* 85:253–261.

Hull, J. and J. Thompson. 1981. Factors which contribute to normalization in residential facilities for the mentally ill. *Community Mental Health Journal* 17:107–113.

Hussian, R.A. and D.C. Brown. 1987. Use of two-dimensional grid patterns to limit hazardous ambulation in demented patients. *Journal of Gerontology* 42(5):558–560.

Hyman, R. 1979. Choosing art for your hospital: Some basic do's and don'ts. *Hospitals* 53(5):95–98.

Izumi, K. 1976. Perceptual factors in the design of environments for the mentally ill. *Hospitals and Community Psychiatry* 27(11):802–806.

Jordan, J.J. 1977. Recognizing and designing for the special needs of the elderly. *American Institute of Architects Journal* 66(9):50–55.

Kahana, E. 1975. A congruence model of person-environment interaction. In *Theory Development in Environment and Aging.* Eds. P. Windley and G. Ernst. Washington, DC: The Gerontological Society of America.

Kahana, E., J. Liang, and B. Felton. 1980. Alternative models of person-environment fit: Prediction of morale in three homes for the aged. *Journal of Gerontology* 35(4):584–595.

Kartman, L.L. 1984. Music hath charms. *Journal of Gerontological Nursing* 10(6):21–24.

Kasl, S.V. and L.F. Berkman. 1981. Some psychosocial influences on the health status of the elderly: The perspective of social epidemiology. In *Aging Biology and Behavior.* Eds. J.L. McGauygh and B.S. Kiesler. New York: Academic Press.

Keith, J. 1982. *Old people as people: Social and cultural influences on aging and old age.* Boston: Little, Brown and Co.

King, R. and N. Ravens. 1968. An operational measure of inmate management in residential institutions. *Journal of Social Sciences Medicine* 2:41–53.

Koff, T.H. 1986. Nursing home management of Alzheimer's disease. *The American Journal of Alzheimer's Care and Research* 1(3):12–15.

Koncelik, J. 1977. Human factors and environmental design for aging: Physiological change and sensory loss and design criteria. In *Environmental Context of Aging.* Eds. T. Byerts, S. Howell, and L. Pastalan. New York: Van Nostrand, Reinhold.

Koncelik, J. 1976. *Designing the open nursing home.* Stroudsburg, PA: Dowden, Hutchinson, Ross, Inc.

Kruzich, J.M. 1984. The chronically mentally ill in nursing homes: Policy and practice issues. Paper presented at the First National NASW Conference on Health. Washington, DC: June 10, 1984.

Kruzich, J.M. and W. Berg. 1985. Predictors of self-sufficiency for the mentally ill in long term care. *Community Mental Health Journal* 21(3):198–207.

Langer, E.J. and J. Rodin. 1976. The effects of choice and enhanced personal responsibility for the aged: A field experiment in an institutional setting. *Journal of Personality and Social Psychology* 34:191–198.

Lawton, M.P. 1983. Environment and other determinants of well-being in older people. *The Gerontologist* 23(4):349–357.

Lawton, M.P. 1981. Sensory deprivation and the effect of the environment of the patient with senile dementia. In *Clinical aspects of Alzheimer's disease and senile dementia.* Eds. N. Miller and G. Cohen. New York: Raven Press.

Lawton, M.P. 1980. *Environment and aging.* Monterey, CA: Brooks-Cole.

Lawton, M.P. 1977a. An ecological theory of aging applied to elderly housing. *Journal of Architecture and Education* 31(1):8–10.

Lawton, M.P. 1977b. The impact of the environment on aging and behavior. In *Handbook of psychology of aging.* Eds. J.E. Birren and K.W. Shaie. New York: Van Nostrand, Reinhold Co.

Lawton, M.P. 1975. Competence, environmental press and the adaptation of older people. In *Theory development in environment and aging.* Eds. P.G. Windley and G. Ernst. Washington, DC: The Gerontological Society of America.

Lawton, M.P. 1970. Ecology and aging. In *Spatial behavior of older people.* Eds. L. Pastalan and D.A. Carson. Ann Arbor: Institute of Gerontology, University of Michigan.

Lawton, M.P. and J. Badar. 1970. Wish for privacy by young and old. *Journal of Gerontology* 25(1):48–54.

Lawton, M.P., M. Fulcomer, and M. Kleban. 1984. Architecture for mentally impaired elderly: A post-occupancy evaluation. *Environment and Behavior* 16: 703–757.

Lawton, M.P., B. Liebowitz, and H. Charon. 1970. Physical structure and the behavior of senile patients following ward remodeling. *Aging and Human Behavior* 1:231–239.

Lawton, M.P. and L. Nahemow. 1979. Social areas and well-being of tenants in planned housing for the elderly. *Multivariate Behavioral Research* 14:463–484.

Lawton, M.P. and L. Nahemow. 1973. Ecology and adaptation in the aging process. In *Psychology of the aging process*. Eds. C. Eisdorfer and M.P. Lawton. Washington, DC: American Psychological Association.

Lawton, M.P., R.J. Newcomber, and T. Byerts, eds. 1976. *Community planning for an aging society: Designing services and facilities*. Stroudsburg, PA: Dowden, Hutchinson, and Ross.

Lawton, M.P. and B. Simon. 1968. The ecology of social relationships in housing for the elderly. *The Gerontologist* 8:108–115.

Lazarus, L.W., B. Stafford, and K. Cooper. 1981. A pilot study of Alzheimer's patients' relatives discussion group. *The Gerontologist* 21:353–358.

Lazarus, R. 1966. *Psychological stress and the coping process*. New York: McGraw Hill.

Leibowitz, B., M.P. Lawton, and A. Waldman. 1979. Evaluation: Designing for confused elderly patients. *American Institute of Architects Journal* 68:59–61.

Levine, N.B. et al. 1984. Existential issues in the management of the demented elderly patient. *American Journal of Psychotherapy* 38(2):215–223.

Libon, A., A. Patterson, and N. Newcomb, eds. 1981. *Spatial representation and behavior: Development and environmental approaches*. New York: Academic Press.

Lieberman, M.A. and S.S. Tobin. 1983. *The experience of old age*. New York: Basic Books.

Lipman, A. and P. Slater. 1977. Status and spatial appropriation in homes for old people. *The Gerontologist* 17(3):250–255.

Luke, E. 1983. Alzheimer's disease: Family support. *Canadian Journal of Psychiatric Nursing* 24(3):9–11.

Mace, N. 1985a. Facets of dementia: Day care for demented patients. *Journal of Gerontological Nursing* 11(1):42.

Mace, N. 1985b. Families: The other side of Alzheimer's. *Provider* 12:22–25.

Mace, N. and Rabins, P. 1981. *The 36 hour day*. Baltimore: The Johns Hopkins University Press.

Marsh, K.J. 1981. Basis for design: A behavioral evaluation of a nursing home environment. Masters thesis, Man-environment relations, The Pennsylvania State University.

McClannahan, L.E. 1973. Therapeutic and prosthetic living environments for nursing home residents. *The Gerontologist* 13:424–429.

Mead, G.H. 1984. *Mind, self, and society*. Chicago: University of Illinois Press.

Melvin, L. and K.G. Gotestam. 1981. The effects of rearranging ward routines on communication and eating behaviors of psychogeriatric patients. *Journal of Applied Behavioral Analysis* 14(1):47–51.

Menks, F. 1983. The use of a board game to simulate the experience of old age. *The Gerontologist* 23(6):565–568.

Millard, P.H. 1981. Last scene of all. *British Medical Journal* 283 (6305):1559–1560.

Millard, P.H. and C.S. Smith. 1981. Personal belongings: A positive effect? *The Gerontologist* 21(1):85–90.

Miler, D. and M. Lieberman. 1965. The relationship of affect state and adaptive capacity to reactions to stress. *Journal of Gerontology* 20:49.

Miller, E. 1977. *Abnormal aging: The psychology of senile and presenile dementia*. New York: John Riley and Sons.

Mitchell, R.G. 1981. Hills of freedom. *Nursing Times* 77(15):640–642.

Montgomery, J.E. 1977. The physical environment of the elderly: Hard architecture. Paper read at the Georgia State Conference on Aging. Athens: May 9, 1977.

Moos, R. et al. 1979. Assessing the social environment of sheltered care settings. *The Gerontologist* 19:74–82.

Moos, R. and A. Igra. 1980. Determinants of social environment in sheltered care settings. *Journal of Health and Social Behavior* 21:88–98.

Moos, R. and W. Lemke. 1980. Assessing the physical and architectural features of sheltered care settings. *Journal of Gerontology* 35(4):571–583.

Morris, M. and M. Rhodes. 1972. Guidelines for the care of confused patients. *American Journal of Nursing* 72:1630–1633.

Mortimer, J.A. and A. Schuman, eds. 1981. *The epidemiology of dementia*. New York: Oxford University Press.

National Institutes of Health. 1984. *Alzheimer's disease: A scientific guide for health practitioners*. Washington, DC: Government Printing Office.

National Institutes of Health. 1983. Progress report on senile dementia of the Alzheimer's type. Vols. I and II. Washington, DC: Government Printing Office.

Nebes, R.D., D.C. Martin, and L.C. Horn. 1984. Sparing of semantic memory of Alzheimer's disease. *Journal of Abnormal Psychology* 11(3):217–238.

Neeman, E., J. Craddock, and R.G. Hopkinson. 1976. Sunlight requirements in buildings: Social survey. *Building and Environments* 11:217–238.

Nelson, M.N. and R.J. Paluck 1980. Territorial markings, self concept and mental status of the institutionalized elderly. *The Gerontologist* 20(1):96–98.

Ninos, M. and R. Makahan. 1985. Functional assessment of the patient. *Geriatric Nursing* 6(3):139–142.

Nissen, M.J. et al. 1985. Spatial vision in Alzheimer's disease. *Archives of Neurology* 42:667–671.

No man is an island. 1981. *Nursing Times* 77(34):1466–1468.

Novick, L.J. 1982. Senile patients need diverse programming. *Dimensions in Health Service* 59(19):25–26.

Oberlander, R. 1979. Beauty in a hospital aides cure. *Hospitals* 58(5):89–92.

Ontario Association of Homes for the Elderly. 1979. *Does it really matter if it's Tuesday? A guide to caring for mentally impaired elderly.* Ottawa: Ontario Association of Homes for the Elderly.

Orr, N. 1987. Nancy Orr: Specialist in special care. *The American Journal of Alzheimer's Care and Research* 2(1):23–25.

Orr, N. 1986. Integrating care improves solution. *Provider* 12:36–38.

Palmer, M.H. 1983. Alzheimer's disease and critical care: Interactions, implications, interventions. *Journal of Gerontological Nursing* 9(2):87–90, 116.

Paluck, R.J. and A.H. Esser. 1971. Controlled experimental modification of aggressive behavior in territories of severely retarded boys. *American Journal of Mental Deficiencies* 76:23–29.

Parmelee, P.E. 1983. Spouse versus other family caregivers: Psychological impact on impaired aged. *American Journal of Community Psychology* 9(4):337–349.

Pastalan, L. 1982. Environmental design and adaptations to the visual environment of the elderly. In *Aging and human visual functions.* New York: Alan Liss Inc.

Pastalan, L. 1979. Sensory changes and environmental behaviors. In *Environmental context of aging.* Eds. T. Byerts, S. Howell, and L. Pastalan. New York: Garland STPM Press.

Pastalan, L. 1977a. Designing housing for the elderly. *Journal of Architecture and Education* 31(1):11–13.

Pastalan, L. 1977b. The empathic model: A methodological bridge between research and design. *Journal of Architecture and Education* 31(1):14–15.

Pastalan. L. 1975. How the elderly negotiate the environment. In *Environment and aging: Concepts and issues.* Eds. M. Bednar et al. Washington, DC: Gerontological Society of America.

Pastalan. L. 1974. Privacy preferences among relocated institutional elderly. In *Man-environment interaction: Evaluation and application.* Ed. D. Carson. Washington, DC: Environmental Design Research Association.

Pentecost, R. 1984. Designing for aging: subtleties and guidelines. *Contemporary Administrator* 6:43–46.

Peppard, N. 1986. Effective design of special care units. *Provider* 12:14–17.

Perry, B.J. 1984. Alzheimer's disease: A challenge to nursing and the care system. *Maine Nurse* 70(1):5–7.

Peterson, R. et al. 1977. The effects of furniture arrangement on the behavior of geriatric patients. *Behavior Therapy* 8:464–467.

Pierman, B.C. 1976. *Color and the health care environment.* Washington, DC: United States Bureau of Standards and United States Department of Commerce.

Pinet, C. 1985. Institutionalized elderly and control over their environment. Milwaukee, WI: unpublished.

Potter A., 1980. In a world of their own. *Nursing Mirror* 150(4):48–49.

Powell, L. and K. Courtice. 1983. *Alzheimer's disease: A guide for families.* Reading, MA: Addison-Wesley Publishing Co.

Prieser, W. 1983. The habitability framework: A conceptual approach towards linking behavior and physical environment. *Design Studies* 4(2):84–91.

Rabins, P. 1986. Establishing Alzheimer's disease units in nursing homes: Pros and cons. *Hospital and Community Psychiatry* 37(2):120–121.

Rabins, P. et al. 1982. The impact of dementia in the family. *Journal of the American Medical Association* 248(3):333–335.

Rader, J., J. Doan, and M. Schwab. 1985. How to decrease wandering: A form of agenda behavior. *Geriatric Nursing* 6(4):196–199.

Rapelji, D., R. Papp, and L. Crawford. 1981. Creating the therapeutic park of the mentally frail. *Dimensions in Health Service* 58:12–14.

Ricci, M. 1983. All out care for and Alzheimer's patients. *Geriatric Nursing* 4(6):369–371.

Roach, M. 1985. Reflections in a fake mirror. *Discover* 8:76–85.

Robb, S.S. and N. Monsour. 1980. Wandering behavior in old age: A psychosocial exploration. Paper read at the 33rd annual scientific meeting of the Gerontological Society of America, San Diego, CA: November 1980.

Robinson, A. and B. Spencer. 1986. Some guidelines for communicating with mentally impaired older people. Ann Arbor, MI: Institute of Gerontology, University of Michigan.

Robinson, A. and B. Spencer. 1985. Some suggestions for self care. Ann Arbor, MI: Institute of Gerontology, University of Michigan.

Robinson, J. et al. 1984. Towards and architectural definition of normalization: Design principles for housing severely and profoundly retarded adults. St. Paul, MN: University of Minnesota.

Rosenfield, N. and A. Wyatt. 1984. Urban nursing home rescued and renovated. *Hospitals* 59:109–110.

Sands, D. and T. Suzuki. 1983. Adult day care for Alzheimer's patients and their families. *The Gerontologist* 23(1):21–23.

Schafer, S. 1985. Modifying the environment. *Geriatric Nursing* 6(3):157–159.

Schlitz, R. and G. Brenner. 1977. Relocation of the aged: A review and theoretical analysis. *Journal of Gerontology* 32:323–333.

Schneider, E. and M. Emr. 1985. Alzheimer's disease: Research highlights. *Geriatric Nursing* 7(3):136–138.

Schulz, R. 1976. Effects on control and predictability on the psychological well-being of the institutionalized aged. *Journal of Personality and Social Psychology* 33:563–573.

Schulz, R. and D. Alderman. 1973. Effect of residential change on the temporal distance of terminal cancer patients. *Omega: Journal of Death and Dying* 4:157–162.

Schwab, M., J. Rader, and J. Doan. 1985. Reliving the anxiety or fear in dementia. *Journal of Gerontological Nursing* 11(5):8–15.

Schweber, M. 1986. Etiologic theories of Alzheimer's disease. *The American Journal of Alzheimer's Care and Research* 1(1):24–31.

Schwenk, M. 1979. Reality orientation for the institutionalized aged: Does it help? *The Gerontologist* 19(4):373–377.

Seligman, M. 1975. *Helplessness.* San Francisco: Freeman Press.

Sheldon, F. 1982. Supporting the supporters: Working with the relatives of patients with dementia. *Aged and Aging* 11(3):184–188.

Snyder, L. 1984. Archetypal place and the needs of the aging. In *Institutional settings: An environmental design approach.* Ed. M. Spivak. New York: Human Sciences Press.

Synder, L. 1978. Environmental change for socialization. *Journal of Nursing Administration* 18(11): 44–55.

Synder, L. 1972. Living environments, geriatric wheelchairs and older persons. *Human Ecology Forum* 3(2):17–20.

Sommer, R. 1974. *Tight spaces: Hard architecture and how to humanize it.* Englewood Cliffs, NJ: Prentice–Hall.

Sommer, R. 1969. *Personal space: The behavioral basis of design.* Englewood Cliffs, NJ: Prentice–Hall.

Sommer, R. and Dewar, 1963. The physical environment of the ward. In *The hospital in modern society.* Ed. E. Friedson. Glencoe, IL: The Free Press.

Sommer, R. and B. Kroll. 1979. Mental patients and nurses rate habitability. In *Designing therapeutic environments.* Eds. Canter, D. and S. Canter. New York: Wiley Press.

Sommer, R. and H. Osmund. 1984. The schizophrenic no-society revisited. *Psychiatry* 47:181–191.

Spencer, B., A. Robinson, and D. Coons. 1986. Difficult behavior and situations. Ann Arbor: Institute of Gerontology, University of Michigan.

Spivack, M. ed. 1984. *Institutional settings: An environmental design approach.* New York: Human Sciences Press.

Sprague, P. 1984. Design considerations for the elderly. *Hospitals* 16:86.

Stevens, P. 1987. Design for dementia: Recreating the loving family. *The American Journal of Alzheimer's Care and Research* 2(1):16–22.

Stevens, P. 1982. Nursing home design focuses on personal needs of residents. *Hospitals* 56:126–127.

Sullivan, J. 1981. Continuity of care between hospital and home. *Nursing Administration Quarterly* 6(1):19–22.

Symonds, R.L. 1981. Dementia as an experience. *Nursing Times* 77(40):1708–1710.

Szpak, L.G. 1982. Coping with Alzheimer's disease. Paper read at the Western Gerontological Society annual meeting. San Diego, CA: February 1982.

Tariot, P. et al. 1985. How memory fails: A theoretical model. *Geriatric Nursing* 7(3):144–147.

Thoits, P.A. 1982. Conceptual, methodological, and theoretical problems in studying social support as a buffer against life stress. *Journal of Health and Social Behavior* 23(1):145.

Tjosvold, D. and Tjosvold, M. 1983. Social psychological analysis of residences for mentally retarded persons. *American Journal of Mental Deficiency* 88:28–40.

Toffler, I. 1970. *Future shock.* New York: Random House.

Turner, B., S. Tobin, and M. Lieberman. 1972. Personality traits as predictors of institutional adaptation among the aged. *Journal of Gerontology* 27:61–68.

U.S. Department of Health and Human Services. 1984. Progress report on Alzheimer's disease. Vol. II. Washington, DC: Government Printing Office #84–2500.

U.S. Department of Health and Human Services. 1984. Alzheimer's disease: Report on the Secretary's task force on Alzheimer's disease. Washington, DC: Government Printing Office #84–1323.

U.S. Department of Health and Human Services. 1987. Losing a million minds; confronting the tragedy of Alzheimer's disease and other dementias. Office of Technology Assessment, Washington, DC: Government Printing Office #OTA–BA–323.

Walsh, D., I Krauss, and V. Regnier. 1981. Spatial ability, environmental knowledge and environmental use: The elderly. In *Spatial representation and behavior across the life span.* Eds. L. Liben, A. Patterson, and N. Newcomber. New York: Academic Press.

Wax, M. 1962. The changing role of the homes for the aged. *The Gerontologist* 2:120–133.

Weber, B., L. Brown, and J. Weldon. 1978. Cognitive maps of environmental knowledge and preference in nursing home patients. *Environmental Aging Research* 4:157–174.

Weisman, G.D. n.d. Wayfinding and architectural legibility: Design considerations in housing environments for the elderly. In *Housing for the elderly: Satisfaction and preference.* Eds. V. Regnier and J. Pynoos. New York: Garland Publishing, Inc. In press.

Weisman, G.D. 1980. Environment-behavior systems. State College, PA: Pennsylvania State University. unpublished.

Weisman, G.D. 1981a. Evaluating architectural legibility: Wayfinding in the built environment. *Environment and Behavior* 13:189–204.

Weisman, G.D. 1981b. Modeling environment-behavior systems. *Journal of Man-Environment Relations* 1(2):32–41.

Weisman, G.D. et al. 1977. Concepts and issues in the design process: Impact of Educational context. *Journal of Architectural Education* 31(1):30–32.

White, R. 1959. Motivation reconsidered: The concept of competence. *Psychological Review* 66:297–323.

Whitehead, C. et al. 1976. The aging psychiatric hospital: An approach to humanistic redesign. *Hospital and Community Psychiatry* 27(11):781–788.

Williams, C. 1984. And this is home? Paper read at the conference on The Teaching Nursing Home: A New Approach to Geriatric Education, Research and Medical Care. National Institute on Aging and the Beverly Foundation. Washington, DC: March 1984.

Williams, L. 1986. Alzheimer's: The need for caring. *Journal of Gerontological Nursing* 12(2):21–27.

Windley, P. and G.D. Weisman. 1977. Social science and environmental design: The translation process. *Journal of Architectural Education* 31:16–19.

Winoground, I.R. et al. 1983. Alzheimer's disease: Assessment of functional status. *Journal of the American Geriatrics Society* 31(12):780–785.

Witcher, S.J. and J.D. Fisher, 1981. Multi-dimensional reaction to therapeutic touch in a hospital setting. *Journal of Personality and Social Psychology* 37:87–96.

Woerner, L. and K. Casper. 1987. Alzheimer's care: A home health model. *The American Journal of Alzheimer's Care and Research* 2(2):23–29.

Wurtman, R. 1985. Alzheimer's disease. *Scientific American* 26:62–74.

Zarins, M. 1982. Psychogeriatric nursing: Making an difference. *Nursing Mirror* 154(10):28–29.

Zepelin, H., C.S. Wolfe, and F. Kleinplatz. 1981. Reality orientation. *Journal of Gerontology* 365(1):70–77.

# Index